Notes From

Daddy

Dr. William H Johnson

Dedication

To all children who struggle to get a good education.

And to the mothers who strive to encourage them.

Go in God's Grace.

About the Author

Having grown up in proximity to many strong and capable men and women, Dr. William Johnson has benefited from interactions and relationships denoting the special connection between generations of like-minded people: especially regarding community improvement.

His span of experience includes 21 years in the United States Air Force, management positions within the Financial and Insurance industries, as well as business ownership, and leadership as a member of the clergy. This life trajectory demonstrates the confluence of many of the desirable characteristics collected along a productive life.

Active in both church and community, Dr. Johnson is comfortable as the lone voice of dissent against the negative elements of society. This reliability for sober consideration served him well during the effort to desegregate Omaha public schools, as well as during his tenure as president of the Citizens Advisory Committee to the Superintendent of Omaha Public Schools.

Doctor William Johnson has been a member of the Clergy ranks for over 35 years, the pastor of two different churches, and the chairman of many church groups. Dr. Johnson is the father of four children: two girls, the oldest is an Educator, and the youngest is a Medical Doctor, together with grandchildren and great-grandchildren. Two young men, the oldest is a Mechanical Engineer and the youngest is a District Court Judge. Doctor Johnson was married to the late Beverly Ann Johnson, who was a Master Social Worker.

The main family has been residents of Omaha, Nebraska, for thirty-five-plus years. Doctor Johnson brought the family home during his time in the Air Force. He is intimately involved in the development of today's youth in every facet of their growth, from birth to adulthood.

Dr. William Johnson also has two Master's Degrees, a Master of Science and a Master of Divinity, and of course, a Doctorate, along with numerous hours of advanced studies in various topics.

Table Of Contents

Foreword

There was a time in our state when the public schools of our town were not integrated. Today, racism and discrimination are allegedly far behind us. However, segregation has left behind an atmosphere of suspicion and distrust between parents and the institutions that are educating children.

This book was conceived when discourse concerning the education achievement gap between racial groups was in full comparison mode in our city. Such discourse led to no fruitful conclusions. However, it did produce innuendos and silent hard feelings between parents and public school staff.

It was during one of these discussion periods that my son wrote an article that depicted the prolonged aggravated grief (PAG) in our school system perfectly. I encouraged him to expand the article into a book. After a few weeks of coaching him to expand the article, he asked, "Why don't you write it yourself?" I accepted the task, and although it has been some years since its completion, I present Henri Harris as an example of such a tortured student.

Grief in education is an area of concern that I had hoped would have caught the attention of the International Classification of Diseases (ICI). Their then latest publication, ICI-11, introduces prolonged grief disorder (PGD) but does not specifically touch on the grief felt by Henri in 'Notes from Daddy.'

The material for this work does not include numbers and statics from noted researchers. Although attention to their labors is appreciated and often put to a practical demonstration in the pursuit of accomplishing this portrayal. The foundation of the observations made here are those observed effects on young people of being repeatedly stigmatized. It has been demonstrated and attested that a climate of hostility transmitted by voice, eyes, and unequal treatment is not conducive to learning. The contention here is that this type of prolonged aggravated grief (PAG) upon an orphaned youth, for theoretically twelve years of public school, may result in a constant state of grief.

The main character of this book, Henry Harris Jr, AKA Henri, lives the life of an orphaned child. Many of the experiences alleged to be suffered by orphaned children in our public-school systems are thrust upon him. It is amazing how many orphaned children there may be among us. It may be safe to say that many orphaned children are not recognized as orphans. Therefore, they are not recognized as needing special attention in their struggles to adjust to the deprivation of a missing loved one at home.

The lack of identification, and therefore understanding of the orphaned population, may well account for the orphaned factor not being considered in the education gap.

Introduction

Melting Pot Vs. Jambalaya

Jambalaya, crawfish pie, me, oh my, oh

Going to have a good time on the by oh.

Hank Williams

My hypothesis is that the much-discussed education achievement gap in our public schools may be explained in terms of grief.

The focus of this book is black male orphaned children. It hypothesizes that future research will show that much of orphaned black boys' educational careers are accomplished while bearing near-crippling remorse brought on by the loss of the male parent. While it is true that grief presents itself upon the loss of either parent, it is the view of this book that it is even more severe when the male parent is absent. The remorse here is the result of aggravated grief brought on, in part, by inconsequential questioning by school staff members.

Such questioning, together with personal devaluation, results in the withdrawal of the student and hinders his ability to learn.

The term orphan here is used to describe a child who has lost a male member of the family for any reason, including sickness and physical or mental disability.

Much attention in investigating the problem of underachievement in public schools has been given by using mathematical calculations and statistical formulas. Future research will show that these methods only measure the dimensions of the problem, not the cause.

For most of our existence as a country, we have claimed to be a melting pot of people. To whatever degree we have been successful, we have succeeded in bringing some people to our shores from nearly every continent in the world. We have communities that are invited, compelled, and uninvited. With each of these people, groups have come with a culture. Simply put, each group has brought a way of thinking with them. The people of this country believed that these diverse communities would take classes upon entry into this country on how to be Americans.

Classes envisioned included how the United States Senate and Congress worked together but were separate seats of authority and power. They would learn of the office of the President and Vice President. Classes would include the Supreme Court and how it functioned. These and other subjects would make them aware of the rights of the American people.

Newcomers would also learn that the American government is a government of the people, by the people, and for the people.

Through successfully passing these classes, they would eventually think like and respect America's cultural values. They would have learned the pride of being Americans. The results would be that they had become a part of a homogeneous people culture, part of a melting pot, Americans.

On the face of it, the plan was and is a good plan. However, the plan contained several flaws that have never been corrected. This book is not intended to catalog the flaws of the plan but rather to account for their inclusion in the resulting mixture. Every culture has traditions, religious beliefs, rituals, stigmas, superstitions, ignorance, and many other characteristics. Just as the meats, vegetables, crawfish spices, and excreta go into the cooking pot, so must this array of unintended ingredients be included in the resulting jambalaya.

One other aspect of the melting pot that should be noted is the Founding Fathers must have assumed that they had none of the particularities mentioned above. Or they may have assumed that whatever their social maladies were, however contradictory they were, would not stand out in the resulting mixture of ingredients. The stark contradiction of this assumption is written in the Declaration of Independence:

All men are created equal...they are endowed by the Creator with certain unalienable Rights, which the founders wrote!

At the time of its writing, slavery was in full bloom; therefore, we must reluctantly add to our national pie prejudice.

It is my understanding that one of the main ingredients of jambalaya is crawfish. What other ingredients may or may not be included depends on who is making the dish. I have been told by connoisseurs of the dish that whatever is included in a particular batch of jambalaya will still be presented as jambalaya.

The main intention of this book is to bring attention to those outliers that have previously operated independently of the constitutional, hoped for sameness of thought, and may be depriving some Americans of freedom in the pursuit of equitable education opportunities. Of special concern is the multiplication effect of these unintended ingredients, and maladies, in our public schools upon many students who have an absent or deceased parent. Outliers are spread by teachers, coaches, and other school staff and associated professionals, intentionally or unintentionally.

Members of these groups are included in the fabric of American society. They have distinguished themselves by contributing to every discipline. They have become soldiers, astronauts, firefighters, doctors, and lawyers. They have contributed immeasurably to the fabric of the United States of America. The melting pot can still be fixed; it's our choice.

The Early Years

Henry Harris eased his Ford Thunderbird 500 onto Interstate 90, headed West toward Cleveland, Ohio, and home. It had been a short trip. Only ninety miles from Erie, Pennsylvania, to Cleveland, Ohio. He would be home for the next three days. His plan was to make effective use of his downtime. There was that touch-up painting his mom had been after him to get at. He also was concerned about the noise in his car that only he seemed able to hear.

Those who really knew Henry shared the saying that Henry was a part of his car. He just was not bolted in. Well, that car and he was on the road together two and three days a week. Henry was an over-the-road salesperson for Hawkins Gas and Oil Company. In addition to gas and oil, Hawkins provided equipment and supplies to oversized truck stops. Most of Henry's customers were located on major interstate highways. Depending on the situation, Henry could travel five hundred miles in a day to take care of Hawkins' company customers.

Henry's official job was to take inventory of station equipment and supplies and fill out reorder requests. That meant that everything that could be used up by the station must be slated for resupply.

The ability of the station to provide timely products and services depended on him keeping the station supplied. Keeping the station supplied directly impacted Hawkins Gas and Oil Company's bottom line. Henry's unofficial job was to give advice to the station owners. The stations had become very dependent upon the success of Henry's advice. Sometimes Station Managers' decisions were delayed for two or three days to run a potential decision past Henry.

Some of the station's associates and employees jokingly remarked that they heard Henry's name as often or more often than their own. There was no question that he was not only looked to for advice by managers but also as a friend.

After a courtesy stop at Hawkins, both to drop off reorder slips and to let them know that he had made another safe trip, he headed home. Now, he pulled into the driveway at home and shut off the car engine. He sat in silence, offering a prayer of thanksgiving to God and Jesus Christ for guiding him safely over the nation's highways. Henry was always grateful for the people he had met and shared with. He always felt that he had received more than he had given and that he had been blessed.

It was important for Henry to discover what the noise that he heard in his car was. It was important to find it before it was time to be on the road again. That gave him two days. The problem was that Henry sensed the noise as much as he heard it. But he knew it was there and that it should not be.

He and the Ford had been many miles together, and they had a feeling for one another. He had two days to get whatever repairs that would be needed. Henry also had two additional very important responsibilities to take care of before his next road trip.

He had been asked for advice on keeping the books by the owner of the Cincinnati station. The owner had been trying to keep the books up himself. He had fallen behind, especially with the payroll tax bookkeeping. Henry had suggested that the station had expanded much faster than anyone could have predicted. Because of the expanded duties, one man could hardly be expected to keep up with the entire operation. He advised the owner to hire an accounting firm with a good reputation to oversee the many accounting functions. The station owner hired the Franklin Accounting Firm, and the firm sent Sara Jean Adams, C.P.A.

Several weeks passed before Henry actually saw Sara and several more weeks before he was introduced to her. There was really no good reason for him to meet an accountant, as their operations did not impact each other. The owner insisted that he meet her. After all, he argued, it was on Henry's suggestion that he had hired her. The least he could do was meet her. Sara was approximately five foot, ten inches tall, in low-heeled shoes. She weighed approximately 130 pounds. Henry decided that she looked very athletically stylish. To say she was attractive would have been a gross understatement. Sara had a way of directing the conversation in just the way that you were glad that it was going. She thanked him for recommending an accounting firm. She shared that she had recommended that the station owner hire a bookkeeper. She had offered Franklyn Accounting to do periodic audits.

The bookkeeper's task was mostly filling in forms that Franklyn Accounting furnished. The station owner's wife noted that a college education was not required as the bookkeeping, by and large, had already been accomplished by the accounting firm. She vied for and got the job. Sara would be on hand for the next several weeks to get the bookkeeper trained and the position established. Sara would be on call for a time to answer questions and to help things run smoothly. The added set-up time and training allowed Henry to see Sara frequently, by chance, and to become better acquainted. They had continued to meet for the past year. He was sure that there might be something in the future for them.

Henry had turned his car over to the garage at the Ford dealer and had arrived at the scheduled time to pick it up. "You were right, Henry," was the salutation he received from the service department attendant. "You saved yourself a lot of walking," they went on. The prefatory was followed by the reasons it wasn't found the first or second, or third time the car had been brought in. They were sure that there wasn't a car dealer that could have found the problem any faster, if at all. He thanked the mechanic and agreed that it had been a difficult problem to solve. Mentally he said to himself one more task down, one to go before tomorrow.

Henry's friendship with Sara Adams had grown into a serious interpersonal relationship.

His upcoming sales trip tomorrow had a two-pronged purpose. His first order of business was to ask Sara to marry him. He was sure Sara felt the same way about him as he did about her. The truth be known, Henry had felt from the beginning that he had found his wife in Sara. The past year was just to give Sara time to get to know him. When he had finally moved their conversations to a more serious level, he found that the station owner and staff had been promoting him from the beginning. As the saying goes, according to Sara: they had gone to the ends of the earth to let her know that he was the greatest. Well, Henry thought he had not needed such encouragement. Although, as he thought back, the station had seemed to need much more accounting help when Henry was due than seemed usual.

The immediate problem confronting Henry was that his mother had been left out of the loop.

He had not mentioned Sara to her at all. To ask Sara to marry him, and he fully expected her to say yes, with his family not knowing her, could be hurtful. Nevertheless, he would try to explain it to his mother as best as he could.

"Mom," Henry began his explanation, "I met this young lady about a year ago. Her name is Sara Jean Adams. She is a CPA that works at Franklyn Accounting in Cincinnati, Ohio."

Henry's mother nodded her head occasionally as he described Sara. He recognized his mother's nod as one of understanding rather than approval.

"She is about 5 foot, 10 inches tall and about 130 pounds in weight. She is a Christian, soft-spoken, and attentive to current local and national events. She regularly attends and supports the local Baptist

Church there in Cincinnati. She is well-liked by her employer and by everyone that she comes into contact with."

He continued, "She does not think more of herself than she should and is always courteous to everyone, especially her elders. She loves children and takes time to recognize them, and they love her."

Henry was finally running out of things he thought his mother would be interested in knowing. He concluded his dissertation on the virtues of Sara Adams with: "I love her; I want to ask her to marry me, and she will be a great mother."

With that, the room fell silent. Mrs. Harris sat quietly, waiting for her son to regain his composure. She could see that his monologue on such a personal aspect of his life as a young lady, and not just any young lady, had been a strain.

"I didn't know if I should ask her to marry me since you had not met her. I didn't want to take a chance on you thinking I didn't respect your opinion or in any way hurt your feelings."

Mrs. Harris paused just long enough to be sure that Henry had said all he intended to say. Then she began. "Henry, from your description of Sara, I couldn't approve of her more without being in her presence for a year or so. She must be a lovely girl and person. You have covered all the characteristics that are of interest to me. I am proud that my son looked at the real value of a person rather than mere transitory. And I'll bet she is beautiful. I look forward to meeting her as my son's fiancée."

Henry ushered his Ford Thunderbird automobile onto the entrance of I-71 and headed south to Cincinnati. He had completed all the tasks that he had set for himself to accomplish. The painting had been accomplished, the car had been repaired, and he had explained to his mom about his oversight in not bringing her into the loop about Sara, his lady.

He had received his mother's blessings for his hoped-for marriage to Sara. Lastly, he had stopped at Hopkins Jewelers and picked up the engagement ring set he had prearranged with them. The rings were both beautiful and stately, matching her athleticism. He did not regret the six months of pay that he had paid for them. After all, they were a symbol of his deep and lasting love for Sara Adams.

Henry arrived at the Cincinnati station just after lunchtime. His appearance aroused the usual questions of why someone would travel such an unscheduled distance. Beneath the curiosity of the why lurked the unspoken suspicion that Sara Adams might have something to do with it. Bob Roberts, the station owner, and manager, asked Henry to stop by before he left the station. He and Henry talked for about an hour and a half, which to the employees left the impression that perhaps Henry's visit was not unscheduled. Bob also asked him to stop back by the station before he departed Cincinnati for Cleveland, Ohio. Henry said that he would be glad to and departed for his next appointment.

Henry's next appointment was more than just an appointment. It was an engagement, a date fixed in time that would be referred to in the Harris family tradition for generations to come. The day in which two people pledged their love to each other and started a legacy of enduring love and devotion. Henry felt in his pocket for the small box with the rounded top. Yes, it was still there, as it had been for the last nearly 400 miles; just making sure, he mused, just making sure. Henry was to meet Sara at Foley's Steak House, not far from the hotel where he would spend the night. He would be a little early by his reckoning, not that he cared if he seemed a little anxious. Heck, he was.

He stepped into Foley Restaurant and paused for a moment to allow his eyes to adjust to the dim lights of the restaurant. To his surprise, Sara was already present. He reflected on his thoughts of only a few minutes ago of seeming anxious and decided her arriving first was a good sign. He had practiced his proposal to her in his head for what seemed like a million times.

The waitress was prompt, giving them only a few minutes for greetings and small talk. Next, they ordered drinks. Orange soda for

Sara and a Diet Coke for Henry, as neither of them drank alcoholic beverages. More small talk and waiting for the drinks to arrive. The drinks arrived, and the waitress was told that they would order later.

Henry rehearsed in his mind: Sara, we have been seeing each other seriously for over a year and a half now, stretching the time by about 5 months. Henry saw the embellishing of the time as fair play, seeing what was at stake.

Henry began, "Sara," drawing her name out slightly and lowering his voice an octave, at the same time, flipping the little box with the round top open.

"We have been keeping company for a little over a year now. I have fallen desperately in love with you. Sara, you would make me the happiest man alive if you were my wife."

There it was. He had said it just as he had practiced it. Now the ball was in her corner. It was her call.

Sara sat without saying a word, her eyes fixed on the box Henry was holding. She had been caught completely by surprise, not suspecting such an event. Slowly her brain began to process that what she had hoped for some time in the future was happening now.

Suddenly and with force, Sara stood straight up from her seat. The force of her standing knocked her chair over backward. The chair fell onto the tables behind them, causing considerable noise and confusion. The neighboring tables spying the ring on the Harris table realized that a proposal of marriage had been made. The surrounding tables began to stand and clap their hands.

"Say yes, say yes!" They chanted in unison.

Sara, having come to a full understanding of the proposal, was rounding the table with arms open. Henry, undisturbed by the clamor, rose to receive what he hoped was his bride-to-be. She simply continued to hold on to Henry's neck. Finally, he whispered to her: "Does that mean yes?"

"Yes! Yes, it means yes," she replied.

By this time, the restaurant began to return to its quiet demeanor with only an occasional pointing reference to the love birds.

The couple was too excited to eat, and after making the appropriate social apologies, they departed the restaurant and drove to a nearby city park. Before daylight showed itself again, they would have planned the next ten years of their lives. Except for their cars and the purchase of clothing, they both had practically every cent they had ever earned. They would get married as soon as possible, as soon as they could purchase a house to live in.

They would live in Cleveland. They would wait to have children for two years. They would try to have as many children as God would bless them with, at least three. They agreed that they wanted a small wedding, spending their money instead to get off to a healthy financial start to their marriage. Above all, they would let their parents express themselves, as much as possible, in their wedding preparations.

Daybreak was threatening over the horizon when Henry dropped Sara back at the restaurant to pick up her car.

"Lock your doors, and don't stop until you get home," Henry instructed.

"If someone runs into your car, don't get out of your car until the police come."

Sara had occasions when she had to return home late, but not this late, so she felt perfectly safe. But it felt good having someone to be looking out for you, especially someone who had just proposed marriage and who had just placed a rather large diamond ring on your hand.

Both of Sara's parents were up when she arrived home.

They scurried around as if they were just up for a glass of milk or glass of water. She didn't give them a chance to ask the usual questions that parents are prone to ask when their only daughter stays out most of the night. She came through the door doing a kind of little jig, turning around in the middle of the floor, and waving her hand above her head so they could see her ring.

Then she added, for emphasis, to the most wonderful man in the whole wide world. Mrs. Adams wanted to know: "How did he propose? Was he romantic? I liked him from the very start," she exclaimed, "I knew he was a keeper," Mr. Adams offered. "I can tell, and besides, he likes the Steelers."

Henry had pulled into the Cincinnati station and parked out of sight. He spent the last two hours of the night sleeping in his car. He awoke before the station came alive and was on hand when Bob Roberts arrived. Bob grabbed a couple of cups of coffee and ushered Henry into his office. Henry waited for the question Bob had asked him to stop by to address.

Bob began: "Henry, I only asked you to stop by so that I didn't have to wait a week or so to get an answer." Henry looked at his friend questioningly.

"How it went last night ..." his friend went on, "What did she say?"

Before Henry could answer, Bob added: "You did ask her, didn't you?

"The night went well," Henry answered, "and she said yes."

"You are an old fox, Bob. You knew all the time why I was here; I don't know how you knew this was the time, but you did. "Can I tell everybody?" Bob wanted to know.

"I mean the station."

"Tell everybody, Bob. I want the whole world to know," Henry replied.

Both sets of parents agreed with what their children had decided concerning their wedding. The children would have a church wedding. The wedding would take place at Enoch Missionary Baptist Church in Cleveland, Ohio. The preachers of both children's churches would perform the wedding. They agreed on a simple wedding reception with a small group of friends in the all-purpose church room. Sara and the mothers agreed on a not-so-simple wedding cake.

In the following weeks, Henry found three houses that he thought both he and his bride would like. She had insisted that she could drive to Cleveland to see them. She would drive up and meet his mother while he was on the road. They could enjoy looking at them together if his mother had time. He agreed with the ladies on the house they both liked best. It was decided, an offer was made, and the purchase followed rapidly. The wedding ceremony was set for three weeks following October 15, 1967.

Henry eased his Ford Thunderbird unto Ohio 3C to Columbus, OH, approximately 141 miles from Cleveland, OH. It would be an easy drive, and with a little luck, he would be back home to Sara by 8 p.m.

He sat the speed control right on the limit of 60 miles per hour. No need to hurry. There was plenty of time. Henry allowed his mind to review his marriage to his wife. He and Sara had been married now for eighteen months, one year and a half. They had been good months with the promise of many more. The parents were of one mind, what was best for the children, which meant no bruised feelings or petty squabbles. The marriage ceremony had gone off as scheduled. The ministers had sorted out who would do what on their own. Reverend Wise had met with them twice for marriage counseling. Sara's minister gave the charge, and Reverend Wise gave the wedding vows.

He was coming up on the Columbus exit. The 141 miles seemed to have melted away in his thoughts. He pulled off the highway and drove the short distance to the Columbus station. The truck stations were always placed with easy access to the interstate. Henry mused that he had learned a lot about station operations in his job. The fact the station owners relied on his opinion in problem-solving increased his knowledge of the problems experienced by stations in general. Henry felt he would be more than prepared for his own station when the time came.

Six hours later, Henry pulled his car back on the highway to retrace his route back to Cleveland and Sara. It had been a quick trip, and he enjoyed being home in the evenings. He was determined to be an at-home husband and father.

Their plan to wait two years before having children had worked out well. Sara would break the news to Henry and the family when Henry returned from his Columbus trip. Henry Jr. would be born in October, almost two years to the day after her and Henry's marriage. Sara had been working for the past eighteen months of the marriage. She had transferred from Cincinnati to Cleveland and still worked for Anderson Accounting. The great thing was that they had saved every cent that Sara had paid. They had also managed to save a good share of Henry's salary. Henry's father-in-law's assessment was that "By anyone's reckoning, those children have done a great job on all fronts."

To say that Henry was ecstatic with Sara's news that they were going to be parents would be a gross understatement. This is one time he could say, "Phone bill be darned, I'm calling everyone who means anything at all in our lives to share the news."

Even in his enthusiasm, he had calculated that he and his sweetheart would be married approximately two years before the baby was born. According to their premarital agreement that meant that Sara would become a housewife on October 15. In his eyes, a far greater occupation than any other. Sara agreed, but with a slight tug at her heart for giving up a chance to contribute financially to the Harris family's hope chest to realize future dreams.

She had Henry's assurance that her job as Mother was far more important and long-lasting than any other she could have.

Henry Jr. was born right on schedule. Henry Sr. was beside himself with glee. When Sara complained that she looked like a mess, her husband assured her that she had never looked more beautiful. Their short marriage had been everything and more than either of them could have hoped for. And now Henry Jr. was healthy and scraping.

What a blessing, what a blessing hoped for and received.

The child, four-month-old Henry Harris Jr., Henri, for short, lay comfortably in his bed waiting for his mom to announce that it was breakfast time. Henri was a large child for his age. He had come into this world at an even 10 pounds, 27 inches. His visitors at the hospital maternity ward consisted of friends of friends and many who were unknown to the family at all. They had come to see the child that had set the nurse's abuzz concerning his above-average size. He continued to grow steadily from birth and continued to show the alertness and animation that thrills all proud fathers.

Henri had been born into a lower-middle-class family with plans of moving up. His father, in solid agreement with his mother, planned to move to one of the better neighborhoods soon.

No way out where those who had their success handed to them lived. Moving out that far would be too much of a contrast between the haves and the have-nots. Besides, that would be reaching too far too quickly.

Henry Sr. wanted a place where his family could live and his child could grow up in relative acceptance. He wanted his son to grow up secure in who he was and expected to be somebody.

It was Henry Sr.'s turn to retrieve his son from the luxury of his temporarily oversized bed. The little one liked the man's smell of his dad. The man's smell and the strength of the arms that scooped him effortlessly from the bed translated into yet not understood feelings of security.

This contrasted with the sudden inhalation of breath made by his mother when freeing him from the gravitational pull of the bed. Even so, it was impossible for the boy to distinguish which he preferred most, the man's smell or the gentleness of his mom. The question, yet not fully formulated in the child's mind, would await nearly a lifetime for resolution.

The Argument

The thought of getting a job was just that, a thought. Now it had grown into much more than that, a real possibility. The local childcare for children five years and under needed help for three hours a day, three days a week. The person hired would cover for the full-time employees during lunchtime and when someone had to be away from the daycare.

A daycare job would be great for Sara Harris. She would be able to take Henri with her. She would be working, and when Henri was not at preschool, he would have additional playmates. With her husband on the road for two or three days at a time, it would help fill the loneliness of being at home. It seemed like a great opportunity to Sara, and she had become more than excited by the prospect of it.

She had decided in her own mind to take the job. Her final decision would come after she had talked it over with Henry Sr. Sara would rely on his judgment. Henry could well see obstacles that, in her excitement, she may have missed. Instead of starting the conversation with, "What do you think? In her enthusiasm, she started it with, "I am going to"

Sara realized her mistake instantly. The shock on Henry's face was telltale. The instant turmoil that her poorly formulated question had fermented in his mind was evident. "What I-I mean is-is," she stammered, but it was too late. Henry's disappointment and hurt were apparent. She had violated one of the first rules of their marriage. "Decisions are made in partnership."

Henry Sr. left the house in a huff. A silly disagreement that never really had time to get underway. Such arguments between husband and wife; are often accompanied by instant regret, except that Henry Sr. was an over-the-road salesman. Today was the beginning of a three-day trip. He would not be able to assure his wife until sometime this evening. At any rate, he thought he would call Sara this evening and smooth things over. Still, he regretted that the whole thing had happened. It was a silly thing when you got right down to it. Hardly something to let cause friction in a family when he would be gone for several days. He resolved within himself to call as soon as he had stopped for the night.

Henry was only several miles from where he had made reservations to spend the night. He was rehearsing his apology to Sara for the third time. Sometimes she would put little Henri up to the telephone, and he would gurgle something that sounded like talking. Henry had no trouble making out the gurgles to mean whatever was comforting to him. Whatever he made them out to mean, Sara would be in complete agreement with him. The memory caused a smile to form on his face and an eagerness in his heart to make things right with the woman he loved.

The Accident

Henry Sr. was nearing his exit off Interstate 71 in Cincinnati, Ohio when the eighteen-wheeler crossed the median at a high rate of speed. The large rig impacted Henry's Ford Fairlane 500 car without any apparent attempt by the driver to slow his big rig down or attempt to avoid Henry's car.

The impact of the crash was followed by an explosion and immediate fire. The police report stated that Henry was killed on impact. The truck driver had suffered an apparent heart attack. A preliminary investigation revealed that Henry's vehicle was in accordance with all inspection requirements and was in proper running order. A complete report of the investigation would follow.

Mrs. Harris waited with pent-up apprehension for her husband to call. She regretted the argument, especially when Henry was about to go on a road trip. But she knew that he would call at the end of his day. It was nearing the end of the day, and she had rehearsed a dozen times what she would say. By now, she was more than willing to take all the blame for the argument. All she wanted was a chance to say, "It was my fault. I am sorry, and please forgive me."

It was getting late, and Henry should have called by now. When the doorbell rang, she ran to it, thinking Henry had come home early. The fact that he would not have rung the bell never entered her mind. She fairly flung the door open. Both to her surprise and terror stood an Ohio state trooper. Mrs. Harris instantly pieced together the reason for the officer's presence. City police officers policed the city; State Troopers policed the highway, and Henry was traveling on the highway. It was apparent to her that this was not simply an informational call.

Her knees could no longer hold her weight, and she sank to the floor amid on rush of tears.

Officer Jeffries had heard the chatter on his police radio of the tremendous accident near Cincinnati, Ohio. He Knew Henry. He and Henry had shared many cups of coffee in the truck stops along the interstate highways. They had become good friends. Officer Jeffries had felt a deep personal loss upon hearing of Henry's death. He did not want Mrs. Harris to receive the information about him by phone or hear it over the radio or television. He had hoped to lessen the shock on Henry's family by delivering the bad news in person.

Suspicions

Four-year-old Henri Harris Jr. lay asleep in his bed, unaware that he had just become, by definition, an orphan. It would take several years for the meaning of that designation to take on its true meaning. For now, it means that there is going to be an emptiness where the man's smell used to be. His mom would do everything humanly possible to fill that space, but there are some things a boy needs to become a man. It is called a loving, caring father.

In the future, Henri's household would forever be categorized as a single-parent home. He would learn that there were many single-parent homes. Some were like his home that once had a father who was married to their mother. But some single-parent homes were because of death, sickness, war, or some other cause a woman was deprived of her husband and a child of a father. He would learn that the world was full of heartless, callous people who treated children that never had a father in the home differently from those that did.

Henri coasted through preschool and kindergarten without talking about his father to outsiders. Even the most callous of stoops draw the line with trying to interrogate an infant. The suspicion would be directed at Sara Harris, whether his mother was being a good mom or rather or not she was ever really married. Did he look undernourished? Had he worn that shirt twice or maybe four times, perhaps all week? These wonderings were a natural prelude to the do-gooders of society to "Do you think she was ever really married?"

Whatever the judgment, Social Services should certainly be called.

It was during one of these Social Service visits that Henri first heard the word argument in connection with his mom and dad. When he asked his mom about it, he could tell that she was startled by his inquiry. Henri could tell that she did not want to talk about it. She brushed it off as 'something silly between husband and wife,' not worth talking about. Henri could see that trying to pursue the question further would yield hard feelings.

One of Sara Harris' greatest fears was that her son would misunderstand her reason for wanting to get a job. He could easily come to the erroneous conclusion that the argument was about him. He was the apple of his father's eye.

To say Henri was the anchor of Henry Sr.'s dreams for a family of not just one child but as many as God saw fit to bless him and Sara with would not be an exaggeration. She just refused to take a chance of tarnishing Henry Sr.'s dream.

Tuesday was the little one's birthday, and his grandmother was coming to visit. She had visited when Henri was about to be born and stayed to help Sara until the joyful day when he was born. She had visited again when he was four years old. It was a sad occasion because her visit was to be present at her son's funeral. This time her visit was to be a joyful occasion.

Hazel Harris was a distinguished, tallish woman of about 66 years of age. She was extremely outgoing, and her love for Henri was genuine and expressive. She smothered him with hugs, kisses, and talk; Henri loved it and her. Even at six years of age, Henri reasoned if anyone could tell him about his father, it would be his father's mom. He loved her all the more because of it.

"Do you like movies?" Hazel asked her grandson. He had never been to the movies or even knew what they were.

"Well, it's hard for your mom to get away, what with work and caring for the home; what was I thinking!" Hazel's reply was careful to avoid the phrase "single parent."

"Well, as long as I am here and if it's all right with your mom, I will take you. Your daddy liked cowboy movies. Gene Autry and Tom Mix. We'll see if we can find a Gene Autry movie."

Henri was thrilled to learn that his father liked cowboy movies. Before the day was over, he would learn that he also liked round chocolate balls, popcorn, and a host of other things, including a cowboy play gun and holster. To his delight, Grandmother Harris just happened to know that he would love to have all the things his dad had liked. His grandmother was a great joy to be around, and Henri learned a multitude of things that a six-year-old can cherish knowing about his deceased father.

Hazel Harris was aware of what Henri was just beginning to go through and endure. Henry Sr. had lost his father to a fever when he was about Henri's age. She had painted a portrait of his father the way only a loving wife can. Yet she knew that regardless of how hard she tried that it would never be enough. She shared as much of Henri's father with him that a six-year-old can grasp. As the years passed, she knew candy, cowboy movies, and play guns with holsters would not be enough.

The task and road ahead she shared with her daughter-in-law. She would do all she could to help and guide her through the rough days ahead. She thanked God that Henry Sr. had married a strong decent Christian woman who was able for the task ahead. Her daughters-in-law's success in raising a healthy boy to manhood depended on three things. A real faith in God, patience, love for Henri Jr., and devotion to Henry Sr.

First Grade

Henri's inaugural entrance into the public school environment went well. He had met all his teachers except for math. Mr. Kelly, the math teacher, was finishing up with a rather severe summer cold. The class was assured that he would return on the second week of school. The math book was handed out by the substitute teacher, Mr. Browning. The book was unusually heavy, and Henri took its weight as an omen of things to come.

Henri's premonition proved to be accurate. Mr. Kelly would prove himself a constant aggravation. Henri's home life, past and present, was a constant subject of conversation for Mr. Kelly. The teacher just could not seem to understand that Henri had a father that had been married to his mother. Or that his father had been killed in an automobile accident. As a result of Mr. Kelly's prodding, Henri was forced to live with his father's death several times a week.

Mr. Kelly's badgering intensified in the second half of the school year. Mrs. Harris could see that Henri was at his breaking point. Out of fear for Mr. Kelly and her son's reputation, she visited the Fairfax Junior High School principal's office. She had requested that all of Henri's teachers be present at her meeting with the principal. Upon her arrival, Mr. Jones, the school principal, had all Henri's teachers seated along the far wall in wooden chairs opposite his desk. He had reserved a cushioned chair next to his desk for Mrs. Harris.

After ensuring that everyone was present, Sara began:

"I am Sara Jean Harris; I was wed to Mr. Henry James Harris of Cleveland, Ohio, on August 4th, 1964. Two years later, my husband and I were blessed with a 10-pound baby boy. We named him Henry

James Harris Jr., Henri for short. He is a first-grade student whom you torment nearly every school day by asking him questions to which you hope to receive proof that his parents lived without the benefit of a marriage certificate and are presently living a fraudulent life.

The extension of this ongoing callousness is that you are attempting to make my son out to be a bastard, and he knows your intent. When he, in his youth, cannot take it anymore, he will lose his temper, and you will want to make him out to be an ill-mannered child from a troubled home. I will not have that!"

Sara began her summary by explaining that she had asked Mr. Jones to make it clear to them that their past conduct must stop. Mr. Jones interjected long enough to wave off those who indicated that they had something to say. Sara concluded by throwing them a fish.

"I am sure you can understand my concerns, and I know you all will want to corporate. Thank you for giving me time this morning to bring these misunderstandings to our attention."

With that, she stood up, and Mr. Jones stood up and indicated that the teachers should stand up, also. Mr. Jones expressed his gratitude that Mrs. Harris had come to the school and assured her that she was welcome to return at any time.

Good Advice From a Friend

Judith Waverly had originally been assigned to investigate complaints at the Harris home and had found them to be baseless. She now stopped by occasionally by invitation. She had become a good friend of Sara. Friendship with Judith also provided Sara with information and guidance concerning current community affairs. Judith was well acquainted with the culture of the public school system. Her friendship provided someone to talk girl-talk with and to "for your information" talk or, as Judith sometimes called it, 'FYI talk.'

After the little bump in the first grade, Henri proceeded through grades two through four with comparative ease. Judith had given Sara a head's up concerning the fifth grade.

"Oh, girl," she had become suddenly excited, "Watch out for the fifth grade. In the fifth grade, teachers like to put a moniker on some children, especially boys."

"If Henri gets a moniker, an alias, you will know because they will use it on his report card first. Sort of like, we have reported it to the parents. This stigma will follow the child through the rest of their school career, and it will affect how future teachers regard him."

Sara was an avid attendee of parent-teacher meetings at Henri's school. Each time he received glowing reports concerning his work ethic. Because of her close relationship with the school, Sara was both surprised and disappointed when first quarter reports were issued. Henri's report record demonstrated that he was excelling in all his subjects. But in the boxes to the right of grade evaluation were boxes that indicated student character traits. Such things as punctuality, friendliness, cooperation with teachers, cooperation with other students, and ability to work with others were indicated by an "S" for satisfactory or a "U" for unsatisfactory. In a space reserved for handwritten remarks was written the word "discourteous."

The Middle Years

Sara Harris arrived at Fairfax Elementary School without an appointment. For once, she would arrive when it was convenient for her, she mused. Mr. Jones had moved on to a larger school that would require more expertise in handling higher numbers of children and teachers. Relative to the nearly five years of the comparative quiet time Henri had enjoyed, he was well worth his new assignment.

Mr. Alexander was the new principal. Sara mentioned that she knew she did not have an appointment but did not apologize. Instead of an apology, she simply stated why she had taken the time out of her busy schedule to visit the school. Luckily, Henri's teacher was in a study period and could be summoned to the principal's office. Upon her arrival, she readily recognized Sara Harris and indicated her pleasure at seeing her again.

His teacher could not imagine what there was about his report record that could have disturbed Mrs. Harris. Without direction, she immediately began to review the many favorable grades reflected on Henri's grade record. Mr. Alexander, yet not fully aware of the problem, seemed content with letting the teacher take the lead in pacifying Sara Harris. It soon became apparent that the boy's mother would not be appeased. Her right forefinger, placed squarely on the offending remark "discourteous."

"What is that? Exactly what does that mean?" asked Sara in a quiet, controlled voice, scarily above a whisper.

"When he, meaning Henri, is asked to answer questions, he becomes defensive and mumbles under his breath," responded the teacher.

"What kind of questions?" Sara followed up.

"About his family. Does he look like his father? How long his parent had been wed?" At this point, Mr. Anderson detected a safe entry point into the conversation. Directing his conversation to the teacher, he asked, "To what subject in the fifth grade do such personal questions apply?"

He pointed out that all she needed to know about her pupils could be found in student records. Such information should be used to form a safe environment conducive to learning.

Mr. Alexander directed the teacher that all references to Henri being discourteous should be removed from school records. He also said that all personal questions concerning Henri's family be directed to the appropriate family member. Moreover, he also expressed that he was certain that all the school needed to know about a student's family would be contained in their registration. After expressing the appropriate amount of indignation, he dismissed the teacher.

Having found it necessary to visit Fairfax Elementary twice in a five-year period, Sara concluded that the school had a culture of maleficence toward single-parent families. She resolved to move Henri to North Junior High as soon as it could be arranged. Mr. Alexander tried earnestly to change her mind. Seeing that her mind was made up, he promised that he would do all that he could to effect a transfer to North Elementary. North would be a good choice because that school went up 'till the ninth grade.

Therefore, Henri would have to change schools one last time before graduation.

The Turbulent Years

The Formative Years

Henri walked swiftly along Broad Street. His head bowed toward the ground as if looking for something. In reality, he was hiding, trying to become as small and inconspicuous as possible. In a few moments, he would reach the bushes and trees that signaled the intersection where Broad Street met 60th Street. That's where the after-school crowd hung out.

Forty paces before he came to the signal bushes that told him he was almost at the intersection, Henri darted to his left and ran.

Staying low, he cut across the park that filled the corner of Broad Street and 60th. He used the multitude of neatly manicured shrubs, trees, swings, and the abundance of children's playthings as cover for keeping out of sight of the hanger-outers. This maneuver accomplished two significant outcomes. It kept him out of trouble with his mom and from answering unwanted questions that were nobody's darn business. Henri didn't think they were such a wrong sort. Well, he thought, there may be a few lousy wannabes, but overall, they weren't the wrong sort.

"Anyway, it doesn't make any difference what I think," Henri mused; his mom had forbidden him. Wrong or not, she had said, "They would take up the time you need to study and do your chores. If you want to grow up to be a man like your father was, you must start acting like him now."

It took a lot to build a man like him; he didn't just turn out that way with any old preparation. It was then that Henri would think to himself but never say it aloud for fear of his life and partly for not wanting to hurt his mother's feelings.

"It would help if I knew something more about my father besides that he died in an automobile accident."

The lack of information you could build on concerning his father was a constant sore spot. Not knowing anything about him is why it is so easy to make me angry, he thought. His dad was dead, for sure, and from a respectable cause. The important thing was that he once had a father who was legally married to his mom. He was not the son of a morally corrupt man who would go around the neighborhood sleeping around. No sir. His father was Henry C. Harris Sr., of Cleveland, Ohio, his mother's husband. Henry Jr. was never intended by his father to be raised by a single parent. He was the victim of unfortunate circumstances that were no fault of him or his hard-working mother. They both had been abandoned through death. If he were to become one with the unwanted, he would require training. A smile came over Henri's handsome face as he mused, "And Mom is doing all she can to make sure that doesn't happen."

The Last Straw

Henri had transferred to North Junior High School from Fairfax Junior High five years ago. His next transfer followed the three or four times his mother had to take off early from work to get him back into class. Henri felt terrible about the strain he had put on her. God knows he had not meant to cause her so much trouble, but it seemed that anything that had to do with him not having a father triggered an intensity inside him that was bigger than he could control. He figured when he told someone that his father had been killed in an automobile accident, that ought to be enough.

But the darn follow-up questions were designed to see if that was what really had happened or something his 'promiscuous' mother had told him. It was like they'd rather his father had died of a gunshot wound or that he had a made-up dad, anything vile and meaner than the truth. Those piss-me-off questions did not just come from MacDaddy kids. Teachers and counselors were just as bad.

God had made him prominent and agile, and he wasn't backing down from anyone. Whether it was the teacher or some annoying classmate. That teacher must have been scared out of his darn wits. Still, he was glad he had not done what he had been thinking to him. It was not the first time Mr. Handily had rushed him with a barrage of questions about what was none of his darn business. Henri had crossed the twelve-foot span between himself and Mr. Handily, scarily touching the floor with the speed and grace of a predator. He had hemmed him in with his big body and the rage that must have been on his face, so his prey couldn't get around him. He had pinned the gym teacher against the lockers so fast, without touching him. The man was terrified out of his feeble mind.

"One more time," the principal told his mother, "one more time, and he is not only out of this school but also out of the system." His mom had tried to stick up for him, but the odds were too much for a woman alone. She said you are going to a different school starting tomorrow or as soon as I can get you into one. One thing is for sure; you are not coming back here anymore, so get everything that belongs to you.

A New Beginning

Martin Luther King Junior High was much larger than North Junior High. His new school was also connected to Martin Luther King High School, which accounted for the substantial increase in size. Henri felt a new sense of belonging in his new surroundings. To his pleasure, his mother described it as an increased semblance of his father.

A reality that was as clear as the second day of gym class. He was big, blessed, and, as his mother described, 'uncommon,' was the doctor's term. Whichever adjective was used, few men could stand next to him without the want of a towel. It meant everything at the time it was discovered.

Henry was an instant celebrity. The fellas wanted him around if they had seen it. The girls wanted to know if it was true. Henry would have preferred to walk through the halls of the high school without the benefit of pants. After gym class, he would purposely wash his hair with his back to the wall—so that all in attendance would get a good long look without the threat of ridicule.

Donna

It was at Martin Luther King Junior that Henri first saw Donna, Donna Rae. He eventually learned her full name. She was tall, with a pretty face and a long ponytail, providing the only clue that she was a girl. It was a full year before Henri had any natural association with Donna, just by chance.

He was walking to the front exit of the school when he first saw her. She was a few years younger than Henri. What caught his attention was that she was being harassed by several young men. They had formed a circle and were playing keep-away by throwing her books to each other in a high arc over her head, just out of her reach. When the book was almost within her reach, they would toss it to the next person in the circle.

'They don't mean her any harm,' Henri thought. They were more motivated by being attracted to her. He was about to go on his way when she dropped the other books she was carrying, and they scattered across the floor. This was the last straw, and Donna's reaction challenged the calamity of Dunkirk and would no doubt survive the test of time in her list of horrors. By this time, Donna was on the floor trying to gather her scattered books, blinded by the cascade of tears that flowed down her face and threatened to thoroughly soak her blouse. Her horror did not deter the young boy's enthusiasm for torturing their truly helpless young victim. Her remaining books came sailing through the air en route to their next agonist's turn to keep the game going. This time, however, Henri's long arms and large hands interrupted its flight, and the game ended abruptly.

Without an invitation for help, Henri scooped up Donna's books and extended his hand to help her to her feet. It was difficult to tell who

44

was the most awed by his sudden entrance into the fray unfolding— the antagonist or Donna. The young men stood as if frozen in stride by the sheer will of Henri's interruption. They remained quiet. Henri's reputation of sexual and social prowess no doubt cautioned them that they were in the presence of nobility. Donna's reaction was one of immense gratitude. She accepted her books from him as he transferred them to her trembling hands without uttering a word. Her awe-struck gaze never leaving his face, she finally managed a feeble, "Thank you very much."

Henri's mother never ceased pointing out that good always comes from doing good. Helping the girl seemed to bear her words out.

In his hurry to get home, he had nearly forgotten his algebra assignment. His heroic act of chivalry changed his focus from the business at hand. With little time lost, it was an easy task to stop by his school locker, retrieve his assignment, and be on his way home.

Henri had quickened his pace to ensure that the delay in his good deed didn't allow his mom to arrive home before him. He had walked a short distance up Broad Street when he saw a girl turn the corner from 60th Street onto Broad Street. Henri remarked to himself that she was going the wrong way. The school was out, and her parents would no doubt be wondering what was delaying her. Henri's interest turned to a concerned puzzlement when the distance between himself and the young lady narrowed. As the small figure became recognizable, Henri identified her as Donna. Henri slowed his steps slightly so that he wouldn't reach his turn-off before Donna was to pass by him.

What would he say to her anyway, he mused. She didn't really know him, and he didn't want to frighten her by questioning her reasons for retracing her footsteps to school. As the distance between them closed, Donna, in an earnest attempt to hide all evidence of her despair, frantically tried to wipe the tears away from her face with the sleeve of her sweater. His concern for possibly violating the local social protocol was dismissed as she acknowledged that she recognized him. She appeared overjoyed by her knight in shining armor's unexpected appearance.

Without prompting, Donna began to reveal the source of her dilemma. She had proceeded up Broad Street and had barely turned onto 60th Street when they had spied her. The bullies were there in much greater numbers than usual.

They saw her coming and began to yell and jump into the air waving their arms and hands over their heads. Panicked by the apparent danger ahead, Donna was wisely retreating to the relative safety of her high school. She would call her father at work from the safety of the school building. It would be a hardship she regretted causing him, but she had no choice. Henri could identify the strain it caused parents to leave the workplace early because of problems at school. He didn't know how often Donna's father had to leave his work early to retrieve his daughter from Martin Luther King Junior High. After reviewing today's experience, he could easily imagine it had been often. It came to mind that the ambush on 60th Street had overflowed from the book-throwing episode earlier in the day.

After determining where Donna lived, they were both surprised to find that they were practically neighbors. Without sharing his thoughts concerning what he considered an ambush on 60th Street, he invited her to walk with him. The relief of not having to call her father was apparent; she accepted his invitation.

They stopped for a moment in the park near a water fountain, and Henri encouraged her to use his handkerchief as a washcloth to wash the tear stains from her face. He also suggested that she use her sweater to hide her tear-stained blouse. Satisfied that her mother would not be overly alarmed at her appearance, both promised to see each other at school tomorrow, and they were off to their respective homes. Donna to 5810 Bradford Street and Henri to 5912 Bradford.

The next day came all too soon. Henri's algebra homework had not come easily, and he had not slept well. To say that he was cranky

46

would have been an understatement. Nevertheless, at the constant coaching of his mother, he had eaten his breakfast and arrived at the school building fifteen minutes early. He was standing on the front stairs of the school building when the black Buick station wagon pulled up. Donna's father had driven her to school. He began to feel a little uncomfortable as he could see Donna pointing in his direction. The man, who he supposed was her father, got out of the car and walked across the street. He was tall about 6 foot 2 inches a good-looking man who talked in a steady, comfortable voice.

He confirmed that he was Donna's father, George Rae, and that Donna was the subject of conversation he wished to have with Henri. He was thankful for the young man helping his daughter yesterday. He spoke in short, concise sentences and quickly gleamed the name of Henri's mother, her address, that Henri's father was deceased, for which he gave his regrets, the fact that the young lad was not involved in extra school activities and that he walked home most days after school. It was established that Henri would not accept payment.

From his mother's several Bible quotes, Mr. Rae could glean a picture of a well-disciplined young man from a good Christian home. It was agreed that on days when Henri was unavailable to accompany Donna home, she would call her father on his cell phone.

After the ambush on 60th Street and the subsequent appearance of Donna's father at school, being seen talking to Henri, word went out that Donna was Henri's girl. Apparently, the bulletin carried with it an advisory that it would be best to stay clear of the young girl, Donna Rae. At least after the word went out, she received no further unwanted attention.

A Glimpse at the Man
Henri

Henri had made the honor roll at school, and his mother had been notified by letter that he was an excellent student. By separate correspondence, she was told that he had been recommended for the prestigious Honor Society. The letter explained whether he was elected to it or not; being nominated was an honor. To his mother, this was a blessing, almost too much for her to have hoped for. It meant that her son was becoming more and more like his father, a lifelong dream. It also meant that Henri might get a scholarship to college. Things looked more than hopeful for the Harris family.

The saying goes, "Into each life, a little rain must fall." The phrase became a reality because of the calm brought by the good news. Henri had waited for Donna like always. The sun was shining, and it was a perfect afternoon that should have made the walk home through the park pleasant and uneventful. Henri had noticed that Donna seemed somewhat subdued but made nothing of it. Midway through the park, Donna could barely withhold the anguish that had been churning inside of her.

Then, Henri realized she had drifted about three feet behind him and to his left. He had stopped to inquire if everything was all right. The question acted to destroy the final constraint guarding her well-groomed deportment. The dissolution destroyed the last shred of her reserve, allowing her to portray the grace of her age and upbringing, resulting in a literal explosion of emotion. It was the explosion that could only be quieted by the understanding of a lover's embrace. Before Henri had a chance to prepare himself for what was to be a life-changing embrace event, Donna was in his arms. The force of her unexpected arrival drove him back a few steps, causing him to stumble over a small twig that had become dislodged from a nearby tree branch. On their way down, Henri desperately grasped at the air as if to use it to stop his fall. Donna continued to maintain her vise-like grip on his neck. They landed in a disheveled heap on the ground.

Up 'till now, Henri's relationship with Donna had been a casual one. He had never even thought about putting a tag on it. The only instance in which he may have touched her was in the exchange of her books at the end of their walk home. Now she lay on top of him as they both were sprawled out on the ground. The buttons on her blouse had become unfastened in the fall. Even though covered by a halter, her breasts did not conceal that Donna Rae had become a young woman.

They both continued to lie where they had fallen. Both were equally stunned and confused by the events that had just transpired. Then they kissed each other as if driven with a passion too long denied. Henri had removed the halter with expertise unlearned, revealing a beautiful sight that almost caused him to lose consciousness. By now, they were long past the point of turning back. With a power that can only be bred into a child by parents of a good stock, with their values constantly as frontlets before them, could such children come back? Yet amid love and lust, Henri found such power in himself. 'We can't do this,' he heard himself say. "We have parents. You have a mother and father, and I have a mother and a father. They want the best for us, so we can't do this. For all we know, we could be making a MacDaddy kid that would be born into misery no matter how smart he was. We must wait."

The whole episode lasted only a matter of seconds. But during those few seconds, their lives had been profoundly changed.

Henry took as much time as needed to ensure that Donna's hair and clothing bore no signs of their experience. Then they continued toward home. Their world had been rearranged. As they walked, he felt

Donna's hand hesitantly grasp for his; he reassuringly allowed his hand to fold around hers. The rumors that had persisted since the book-throwing incident at Martin Luther King Junior High School finally came true: "Donna is Henri's girl."

Despite being delayed in the park, Henri was relieved to have reached home ahead of his mother. He quickly went, scarcely reaching his bed, before allowing his colossal body to fling itself across its surface. Even though he had learned to lay diagonally across its surface, Henri's feet still managed to protrude well beyond the limits of the bed's ability. As he began to relax and consider the events of just minutes past, he allowed his mind to retrace the event in the park with detail. One thing was for sure; Donna was not just someone her father had arranged to protect his daughter from the elements of the world anymore. In just an instant, their relationship had gone well beyond that.

It was a fact that they both had been carried away as if on a sudden tsunami wave of passion. What had happened could not be called an incident. It wasn't that by a long shot. What had happened had changed their understanding of who they were. One thing for sure was that she was not just the little girl that lived on the next block anymore. But what was the difference? Better yet, was it permanent? He sure could use Henry Sr.'s advice right now. Well, he might as well own up to it; Donna was in love with him. The question: " Would it last?" was paramount because he had already subconsciously admitted to himself that he loved her.

Presenting Her Case

Henri had decided that he would not say anything concerning the incident awakening in the park the previous evening. When her father's black Buick arrived at school the following day, he greeted Donna as always. Gathered her books as always and walked with her to her day's first class. He would not see her again until 3:15 pm at the front gate of the school that day. The verbal exchanges between himself and her father consisted of a professional wave of his hand to Henri, a nod, and a genuine smile.

The end of the school day was a long time coming. Donna was punctual; arriving with the usual accompaniment of a book, they were off toward home. It wasn't until they had entered the park that Donna broke the silence.

"I know that I acted scandalously yesterday," she began. "My father had told the family that he was being promoted. He described it as something that everyone works for and hopes for. My only problem is that we have to move at the end of this school year. I had to tell someone why this was such a tremendous disappointment. I was happy for my father and my whole family. But I also realized that moving meant that I would be leaving you."

There it was. Henri remained silent, waiting for Donna to explain further.

"There was no one I could tell my feelings to without explaining why," she went on. She still had not said the words that Henri wanted to hear. However, he waited quietly, fighting back any expression of impatience that tried to be heard before its turn.

"Henri, I know that you probably didn't know what this was all about before yesterday."

Henri could listen to the change in the pitch and sound of her voice. It was the sound he had heard in his mother's voice when she started remembering the little personal things about his dad. But he still didn't help her reach her point. He needed to hear it from her—right out and in plain English.

"Henri, when we first met, I was a little girl running from everything that was mean or looked mean in the world. You have protected that little girl from the book-throwing incident until now. But Henri, I am not a little girl anymore. I am almost ready to graduate and go into college or some vocation."

Donna made her case in a manner befitting the form of Johnnie Cochran. She summarized with equal effectiveness: "Henri, I've grown up, and I love you."

Henri signaled that she had won her case by reaching out and drawing her to him. They kissed there in the park for what felt like an eternity.

Moving Day

With the deadline established, time seemed to hurry by with a vengeance. Donna had no qualms about letting the world know that Henri was taken. When they walked, even in the halls of Martin Luther King High School, her hand would find him, and they would walk hand in hand. Finally, no matter how hard they tried to hold it back, June came, and the school year ended. Everything that needed to be completed was. George Rae loaded his family into the black Buick station wagon. Donna had told Henri the time they would depart so he would be on hand to wave them goodbye. Mr. Rae, with the punctuality of a Swiss watch, came by the house at the appointed time. Mr. Rae slowed his car to a dignified pace that no doubt appeased his daughter. Mr. Rae and Donna's mother waved and smiled respectfully from the front seat as they passed by.

Amidst tears and blown kisses, Donna waved frantically from the car's back window; then, they were gone.

Henri, already feeling the loss of Donna, sought refuge and solace in his room. The bed groaned under his increased demand upon it. Yet, it had remained the reliable refuge it had been when the terrors of being fatherless roamed in the night shadows, bringing omens of doom yet to come.

Spring Break

Henri could not deny that Donna's departure had taken some of the magic out of spring. However, it would soon become apparent that the rest of the world was moving at its usual pace to get to wherever it was going, and it would carry him wittingly or unwittingly along with it.

We are getting a new neighbor, Mrs. Harris announced. Her tone was mixed with both enthusiasm and dread at the same time. With the eagerness that the new neighbors would be a welcome addition to a harmoniously quiet community, there was also dread that they would be just the opposite. The neighborhood had only experienced one family moving as far back as Henri could remember. The thought that it was Donna's family brought a surge of melancholy to Henri's heart, which he immediately rejected. He was not about to let self-pity and remorse ride with him through the summer months.

The new neighbor was tall, not quite as tall as Henri, but a soft-spoken, well-built, athletic man. He was not a weakling either, Henri observed. The man carried heavy things with ease. Some heavy things included a refrigerator, clothes washer, and dryer. At his mother's prompting, Henri volunteered his services in unloading the big moving van. The van was a double length, and a man would indeed feel the need for assistance before the job was completed. During the unloading, the men became well acquainted.

The new neighbor was Jackson Brown, formerly of Pittsburg, Pennsylvania. More recently, Jackson, the men were on a first-name basis now, a wide receiver for the Cleveland Brown football team. Jackson's wife's name was Brenda; they had three children: Robert, Mark, and Christine.

Despite their age difference, Jackson and Henri became good friends during the following weeks. The man was amazed that Henri knew next to nothing about the football game and took it upon himself to correct what he called a travesty. The park became a field of learning where Jackson would pass on as much of his twelve years of professional football experience to Henri that could be absorbed during summer vacation. How to time his speed to the football trajectory to successfully complete a pass? How to successfully complete a poorly thrown pass using his height and ideal arm length? What pleased Jackson the most was how Henri had picked up on catching the ball one-handed, with either hand. Jackson was sure this would set Henri apart as a potential wide receiver on any football team.

The letter from the National Honor Society arrived in a sizable, prestigious-looking envelope. The envelope was embossed with large protuberant lettering proclaiming the aloofness of the sender. Mrs. Harris was tremendously impressed before the envelope was even opened and its contents revealed. After the envelope was opened and the purpose of the content had been read and reread, her eyes filled with tears of joy. Henri had been selected as a member of the National Honor Society for his senior year.

The envelope carried good news for the Harris family. To Henri's mother, it was an affirmation of her hard work in raising Henri. It also attested that she did not need assurance except in her heart—Sara Harris was a good mother. In Henri's eyes, good was not a strong enough word. Sara Harris, Henri Harris' mother, was a tremendous mother.

Coming of Age

Henri was fast approaching his full complement of physical prowess. Exercise and clean living, together with parental hereditary contributions, were shown in his physical presence.

Over the past months, he had grown to his fully allocated six foot four inches height. His body had become a living sculpture of hardened muscle as if sketched out by Michelangelo and chiseled into his body with the skill of the gods. He moved with smooth, even unhurried steps that propelled him forward with effortless grace. Henri had learned from studying famous men, especially black men, a brace of attributes he thought had favored prominently in their success. He was determined to mimic these same attributes in developing his own worldview.

The first step in developing the persona of Henri C. Harris Jr. adult male was humility. Over the summer, he realized that the unflattering questions concerning his parentage were designed to diminish him. His actual defense was kindness and the use of a well-developed command of the English language. For that, he developed a long vocabulary list and studied it diligently. This, together with a significantly improved knowledge of the English language, would serve him well in reaching the goals of his newly acquired persona. To his credit, he cared to gauge his choice of vocabulary and grammar to the age group and occasion in which he found himself.

Henri had seen the fear in the eyes of adult males, predominantly white males when he approached them too directly. Young men his age took great pride in showing off their muscular development. They wore tight, short-sleeved shirts that exhibited their bulging muscles.

Henri took every precaution to avoid this trap. He had taken a page out of Mr. Rae's fashion book. His clothes, very much in step with his age group and station in life, did everything possible to accomplish two things. First, he wanted to hide the blessing that God had given his physical structure. Secondly, he wanted his dressing to be in step with his peers while at the same time distinguishing himself to be worth a second glance.

The third part of his persona was already in place. He had many sayings passed on to him by his mother, like the sayings that had quickly convinced Donna's father, Mr. Rae, that he could be trusted to walk his beautiful young daughter home after school. That was a marker because Henri could tell Mr. Rae was a brilliant businessman. The conversation with Mr. Rae had only taken a few minutes. Henri was sure that his favorable decision was based on Henri's bearing. His bearing was gleaned mainly from his mother's insistent teaching and self-portrayal of the wisdom sayings found in the Bible.

It was Sunday morning, and Henri's mother had asked him to wear the one pair of dress pants he owned. She had also suggested that the plaid sport coat would go well with the brown pants. Henri obediently did as he was instructed, even though he had no idea the occasion for all this fuss. A visitor, he mused to himself; some high mucky-muck that occasionally made their presence felt around school startup time, especially since his mom was a single parent. The social services seemed to think it was their responsibility to check and see if single mothers were raising their children in the proper environment. Henri could well have chosen a few choice words that were not fitting to his newly acquired persona but restrained himself.

"Are you ready?" Henri's mother called. Her voice carried the same urgency that signaled he was in danger of being late for school.

"I'm coming, Mom," was his reply. He arrived at the foyer leading to the front door to find his mother dressed in her wardrobe's most impressive attire. Henri had seldom seen his mother dressed in such a fashion. No-nonsense attire for work and shopping were the usual luxuries that she permitted herself. Sara Harris was a beautiful woman, he mused to himself.

Henri seldom had to ride in the family car. Since school was within easy walking distance from home, there was no necessity for motorized transportation. The old Honda seemed like it would last forever. Mrs. Harris backed from the drive and straightened the car in the street before she announced their destination. "We are going to church," she said.

The sign identified the church as the Enoch Missionary Baptist Church of Cleveland, Ohio. The smaller black lettering at the bottom of the sign identified the church pastor as the Reverend Bernard P. Wise, D/Min. The church building was a stately-looking brick and stone with a well-manicured lawn and shrubbery.

Henri and his mother made their way from the mid-parking lot toward the church entrance. Henri's mother was greeted with a "Good morning, Sister Harris." "Good to see you again; is that little Henri? My, he has grown," together with a host of other greetings. The primary entranceway was designed in a manner that gave a welcoming feeling to Henri and his mother as they approached the church.

The inside of the church kept the promise offered by its stately architecture and well-maintained grounds. Upon entering a large, beautifully designed room with colored glass and an arched ceiling that Henri learned later was the sanctuary, his church experience began.

At the far end of the cover was an elevated section or platform. In front of the venue was an ornate podium for people to stand and speak. Behind the stage was a row of elegantly furnished chairs that were the places for Reverend Wise and associates to sit. Behind the unique chairs was an ornate railing about three feet high. The bar was furnished with an elegant curtain so those sitting behind it would only be visible from the waist up. Behind the railing, several rows of seats were placed in an arch shape.

On one side of the platform was an organ instrument, and on the far side of the platform, across from the organ, was a piano. There was also an enclosed area on the platform made of what Henri supposed was Plexiglas. Inside the enclosed space, Henri thought he could see a drum set.

Another ornate railing, approximately three feet high, was about ten feet in front of the platform. This railing was equipped with a matching curtain like the one on the forum. From the second railing and extending to the entranceway of the church was a sea of seats for the accommodation of the parishioners that would come to hear Reverend Wise preach God's word.

Reverend Wise was brief but thorough in his presentation of God's word. To Henri's delight, Reverend Wise covered in thirty minutes what he regarded as the essential elements of the Bible. Of course, Henri mused, he would require further study. At least he had a fertile foundation upon which to build. Despite his evident superior education and research, Reverend Wise presented the creation of heaven and earth, of the sea; animal; and plant life in an easily understandable manner. His presentation also included the creation of humankind, the fall of man, the earth, and the birth of spiritual man. He acknowledged that he had left some gaps in his presentation and supplied a handout at the end of service as an aid for those interested in filling them in.

After service, Reverend Wise requested a brief word with visitors. He introduced himself to each and asked a few straightforward questions to ascertain their religious preference and prayer needs. After he had spoken to each visitor, they were invited to partake in a luncheon being served in the church dining room.

Henry was the last to speak to Reverend Wise. He only asked him if he had any prayer requests. Henry did not, so he gave the boy a very elegant-looking Bible. The Bible was made of genuine leather and had raised letters 'Brother Henry C. Harris.' Reverend Wise, to his credit, could see the complaint forming in Henri's mind.

"It is not an exaggeration to say that your father was a great man and your mother an exceptional woman. I can see that she has cultivated as much of your father in you as possible for one person to do for another. My observation is that you have the stuff to bring their and God's aspirations in you to fruition."

With that, he invited Henri to share dinner with the church, and he was off to see to his many duties.

The trip home was as quiet as the one coming to church. Henri's mind was full of questions and puzzlements. Mrs. Harris avoided asking the usual boring questions, "What did you think of this and that? Did you enjoy Reverend Wise's presentation?" and a host of other questions without answers. Instead, she left Henri to consider all he had seen and experienced.

He would soon enough, in his own time, come to the point where questions would be formulated and eventually asked. But for now, the prospect of entering his final year of school was foremost in her mind and Henri's. All else would have to wait.

The Senior Year

The school year started as usual; everyone was anticipating and surprised at its arrival. The hustle and bustle with the regular frantic momentary lateness abounded. Henri's mother seemed to be the only one in town with the calmness to meet the demands of the occasion. She had called him with that familiar sound in her voice that signaled that he was running late. As a result of her urging, he arrived at school and was seated in his first classroom twenty minutes early.

Henri's first class of the day was English comprehension or just plain old English Comp for the old-timers. Since he was the first to arrive, he had the pleasure of watching each student enter the room. This became a valuable pastime for him as it gave him a chance to feel the persona of each of his classmates without appearing to stare. As a result of this unexpected opportunity, he was able to muse as to who was a genuine person and who was untrustworthy.

Henry had four classes, all of which were advanced subjects built on lessons he had begun in elementary school. His classes were preceded by the word "Honors," i.e., (Honors) geometry and then a number; (Honors) English Composition, etc.

By the end of his first day of being a senior, he felt confident about his subjects and instructors. Being a senior was going to be a breeze.

A Game Changer

Henri had just exited the school's main entrance when he saw the ball climbing into its arch before making its descent to the ground. He judged that its impact was going to be in the midst of a class of elementary students being dismissed from the Martin Luther King Jr. elementary school next door.

Henri had increased his pace to reach the spot where he calculated the ball would impact the ground. His calculations were correct, but the children hindered his speed, and he would be just short of where he should be to interfere with the ball's trajectory. Thanks to his time spent with Jackson Brown, Henri could veer to the side of the child that would be the recipient of the ball.

And reaching out using his large body and long arms, he caught the ball with the only hand that could be there in time to impede a disastrous outcome. Henri gracefully tucked the football into his arms and threw it back to the now terrified originator of the would-be tragedy with the same graceful movement.

Henri quickened his steps to make up for the time he had used to accomplish the good deed at school. It was time well spent, even though the child's mother would never know how God had blessed her this day. He had already made his turn and was well on his way across the park when he heard the call: "Young man, young man."

Henri kept walking. Glancing over his shoulder, he saw a middle-aged, casually dressed gentleman. By now, he was pointing in Henri's direction and continued calling, "Young man, young man."

Henry stopped and waited for the man to reach him.

The man reached Henri and signaled that he needed some time to catch his breath before he would be able to talk. Henri waited patiently without showing any impatience.

After a few minutes, the man began to make himself known to Henri. He was Bob Rhodes, a football coach. He was new at Martin Luther King Jr. high school, so Henri probably didn't know him. Mr. Rhodes had seen Henri make "that one-handed catch" and wondered how long he had been playing football. Mr. Rhodes seemed astonished and disappointed to learn that Henri had never played football. Adding to the coach's bewilderment was the news that Henri had no intention of trying out for the team.

Henri explained that he had been elected to the National Honor Society during the summer months. He was hoping to win a scholarship to college through academic achievement. Henri explained that his father had been killed in an automobile accident when he was a child. His was a single-parent household. His mother depended on Henri to get a scholarship to further his education after graduating from high school.

Mr. Rhodes was an experienced athletics recruiter and quickly recovered from what looked like a blind alley. His first try was a traditional tried and tested allurement. With Henri's size and dexterity, he would excel past his competitors to become a celebrity. Mr. Rhodes saw that stardom did not trump the best chance of getting selected for a scholarship. Therefore, he offered, with greater success, football as a backup plan to the same end.

Henri thought the backup plan had some merit. He offered to talk it over with his mother and get back to coach Rhodes the next day 'if possible.' Henri had learned that it was not for him as a juvenile, under the guidance and supervision of his adult mother, to make concrete life decisions or promises. He would try to broach the subject with his mother, and if she had time, they would discuss it.

Mrs. Harris had arisen well ahead of Henri this morning to get him off to school. While Henri was in school, his mother had been working an eight-hour shift that required her to be on her feet most of the time. It was no understatement that she might not feel up to such an important decision.

Mrs. Harris was always interested in knowing as soon as possible anything that touched on the life of her only son. After removing her shoes and finding a comfortable place to rest her body, she said, "Now, tell me everything that happened today, and please don't leave anything out."

Henri started from the beginning, with him arriving at school twenty minutes early. He explained how his early arrival had allowed him to observe each student as they arrived for class.

He explained that although they would not be with him in every category, he still considered it useful. He told her about the one-handed catch while leaving the school grounds. She agreed that it was a good thing. Of course, she repeated that good things come back to those who do good. Finally, he told her about Coach Rhodes and his invitation for Henri to play football. He also told her how the coach presented football as a possible source for a scholarship.

Mrs. Harris listened quietly, nodding her head in agreement from time to time. However, she did not shake her head as Henri explained his meeting and conversation with Mr. Rhodes.

After a few minutes pause that seemed like hours to Henri, she began: "Henry, you are still in high school, but you have become a young man. You had kept your lessons up even before we came to Martin Luther King Jr. Since you have been at this school, you have learned to control your temper and have had no difficulties with pupils or school staff. You were entrusted with the care of Mr. and Mrs. Rae's daughter, Donna, for the past years.

You think things through before you act and ask questions when needed. Reverend Wise could see that in you, and so do I. It is good to seek advice from those adults around you who have earned your trust and respect. Of course, I am always here for you when you feel that you want to talk things over. This proposal from Mr. Rhodes is yours to decide. We are talking about your future. Lord knows I want the absolute best God finds in His infinite mercy to give you. But I feel that in this case, you are the only one who can make a truly wise choice."

The Choice

The school counselor was Miss Rose Barnett. Miss Barnett was also the caretaker of scholarship information. She knew who was giving college scholarships and many skill training opportunities.

Henri requested through the principal's office to see Miss Barnett. Henri's last class of the day was Honors Geometry. During this class, a principal's helper from the elementary school was there. He brought a note to the instructor. Henri had a meeting with Miss Barnett at 2:15 pm. That was fine because he had promised Mr. Rhodes an answer to his inquiry today if possible.

Of course, he had to endure what Henri perceived as a collage of unnecessary questions. There were only two forms. The first involves personal information, name, date of birth, school year, and address. The second form gathered academic information, subjects studied, and class ranking.

Miss Barnett is a young woman, about 26 years old. She was very cheerful even during this time of the school day. She looked fresh as if the first bell of the day had just rung. "Come in, Henri." She exclaimed, "You are interested in college scholarships?" Miss Barnett had a form in front of her with several boxes that were apparently to be filled in. As she asked Henri questions, she would scribble his answer into one of the boxes. What would you like to study in college was the next question. Who knew for sure what they wanted to learn? Henry mused to himself, "I am interested in Law, primarily," he replied. "However, I am also interested in anything related to mathematics. I have successfully studied honors differential equations, geometry, and statistics. I am also a member of the National Honors Society."

Miss Barnett looked over the form on her desk at the multitude of information she had received from Henri and placed it in the appropriate boxes. After several minutes she pushed her chair back from her desk. Again, she retreated from Henri's presence in thought.

Then she began, "You have a very impressive school record. Ordinarily, I would be able to almost promise you that you will get a scholarship. But as you know, we are in a national economic slowdown. As a result, parents who ordinarily pay for their children's education to as prestigious schools as possible are instead vying for a scholarship to any college they can get into."

Miss Barnett paused as if to shift gears and said, "Henri, this means that New York and Florida parents are applying for scholarships in states like Pennsylvania and New Mexico. These students are also honor roll students. This, coupled with the personal wealth of many of these parents, makes winning a scholarship doubly difficult in the upcoming rush. Rest assured, we will do everything possible to secure a scholarship for you. It is good for you and Martin Luther King high school to get as many scholarships as possible for our students."

Choice Delayed

Coach Rhode was waiting for Henri at the door of the principal's office, hoping to talk to him before he left the school building. He asked if he could walk with Henri simultaneously, and he said he would not delay any time constraints the boy might be under. A man of his word, he matched Henri's stride, and they proceeded up Broad Street toward the park.

As they walked along, Henri shared with Coach Rhode that he had sought out Miss Barnett for scholarship information. The Coach said it was best to gather as much information as possible before making a life-altering decision. He understood that considering Henri's conference with Miss Barnett, he likely needed more time to think about what was best for him and his family.

Mr. Rhode made good on his promise not to interfere with Henri's time constraints on returning home. Their conversation carried them nearly halfway across the park. They concluded their discussion with mutual understanding and respect for each other's goals and responsibilities. Henri to himself, his mother, and his deceased father. Coach Rhode to himself and Martin Luther King High School.

Decisions

Arriving home well before his mother, Henri quickly went to his bedroom to find solace with his old friend. But his old friend had become a hugely undersized bed. Nevertheless, Henri sprawled diagonally across its circumference, extending his feet a full three feet beyond its ability to accommodate them. He lay with his eyes fixed toward the ceiling, seemingly seeing beyond it, through the roof into space. The quiet of his room and the comfort of the bed that had resolved his fears of demons and a thousand imagined terrors through the years melted away his indecision. 'Making decisions is not as easy as it sounds,' Henri mused to himself.

He had not fully realized how many people could be affected by our decisions. He was the only one who would play football, sure.

Yet, he could see more clearly now past the scholarship. Henri could see that even without the scholarship, a larger responsibility loomed. Responsibility for a decision that had already been made. He had never thought about the ones who had made these decisions so clearly. The ones who persevered in making it possible for him to be allowed choices.

Henri felt that his decision-making process had benefited him with an unmistakable surge in intellectual maturity. At least, he hoped so. He certainly felt much more able than he did when he first sought the solace of his old friend. Still, he realized he was far from the yonder shore and cautioned himself not to overstate his capability.

Still, he liked the feeling of being permitted to make his own life-shaping decisions. Being assured by Reverend Wise and his mother added to his decision-making confidence. All the same, he cautioned himself, always seeking competent advice.

Henri's mind began to meditate on the multitude of persons, living and dead, cheering in the wings for him to be assertive and cautious. His mother would be at home or on the sidelines, fearing for his safety. He owed Henry Sr. for helping to make him the kind of man he hoped to become. Sure, he was deceased, but he was very much alive in the Harris family. His mother saw that Henry Sr. was the model, and his wife was the caretaker of it.

The sound of the telltale squeak of the door that had betrayed Henri in his youth when secrecy became all-important now announced that his mother had returned home. He rolled off from the bed, his strength having been renewed by the resolution of the pros and cons of his future endeavors.

Let's Play Ball

Mrs. Harris sat silently across from her son. True to her word, she did not ask if he had made a decision or what it was. She waited patiently for Henri to choose the words he was most comfortable with to start their evening talk.

He started by sharing the people he had consulted with in arriving at his decision. He had spoken with Miss Barnett, the school counselor, about his academic scholarship prospects. She had made her observations in light of the current economic slowdown. Despite Henri's excellent academic record, his chances for the scholarship were greatly diminished. Coach Rhodes felt that football would be a good backup plan if economic circumstances precluded plan number one. Henry had confided in his neighbor, Jackson Brown. Jackson was a former NFL football player. He also played the position of wide receiver, which Henri would be playing.

Mrs. Harris sat silently, occasionally nodding to indicate that she understood what her son was saying. But not necessarily that she agreed or disagreed with his methods or the content of his reasoning. Whatever Henri decided, his mother would be one hundred percent behind him. Finally, Henri concluded: 'The bottom line, Mom, I have decided to play football.' It went without saying, but Mrs. Harris said it anyway.

"You have my full support in this and whatever you do." She crossed the space that separated them in one graceful move and embraced her son.

Gearing Up

Mr. Rhodes was delighted to hear that Henri had made a favorable decision to play football. Football season was fast approaching, and a thousand tasks were to be completed. Of major concern were the fundamentals of becoming an outstanding wide receiver. There was also the playbook. There were a multitude of standard plays that must be memorized. In addition to the classic plays, many plays would be designed on the field. The on-the-field plays would have to be comprehended and executed in real-time.

Henri also had to become aware of the rules of the State and National High School Associations. In addition to these, the state and national associations of his high school athletics' departmental rules and regulations. He learned that there were rules of good sportsmanship and personal conduct off the field. Coach Rhodes cautioned especially against those who would try to attach themselves to athletics, especially successful athletics.

In addition to the fundamentals of the game, learning of standard plays, the type of form the team would play, relevant association rules, team rules, and organization, there was practice. When the school day ended, football began. The coaches tried to include everything in practice that they may encounter in a real game.

Perhaps the greatest influence on the effectiveness of Henri's football career would be Jackson Brown.

He had said, "The quarterback's job is to throw the ball. Your job is to catch it. It doesn't matter how well he does his job; to be an outstanding wide receiver, you must excel in doing yours."

Henri understood the connotations of what Jackson was saying. In a nutshell, "No matter how shabby the pass or how far off the mark, catch it! Regardless of the play, put yourself in a position to receive the ball. That means even if the play does not involve you, be as useful as possible, but always ready to receive the ball should it be thrown your way."

When the after-school practice was over, Jackson was there to walk home with Henri. The walk home consisted of insights that made the points covered in the course of practice come alive for him. He listened intently as his neighbor poured out as much of his years of experience with pro football as he thought Henri could absorb in his budding career.

Henri's first game came on a Friday evening. His fan base was present in full strength, his mother and Jackson Brown. To his surprise, Jackson's wife, Brenda, was also there. Secretly, he would be more than happy if his mom and Brenda had been unable to make the occasion. After all, he mused, "You could turn out to be a jackass— it is your first game."

The quarterback, Roger Thomas, was a slightly built young man about 6'2' tall. This season would be his fourth year of playing football. He had transferred to Martin Luther King two years ago. He immediately won the position of starting quarterback. No doubt that was the reason for his transfer. Roger could throw the ball well if he weren't hurried. If hurried, according to Jackson, he was prone to make serious mistakes.

Like they say, 'Haste makes waste.'

Henri found him to be of an amiable disposition. Roger, the one who was more experienced on the football field, did his part as a quarterback to create cohesiveness among the players.

Play Ball

At last, it was time for the game to get underway. Jackson had warned Henri about the butterflies in his stomach. He had assured him that they were a good thing. He had said that they always left him with the kickoff.

Henri found that this was true for him as well. He started the game on the bench and remained there for the first and second quarters of the game. The bench time allowed him to watch the game's ebb and flow. But by the end of the second quarter, he became impatient to get into the game.

During half-time, Coach Rhode encouraged the team to remember the fundamentals they had learned during practice. He pointed out that Martin Luther King had a better defense than the opposing team. It was the offense that needed to provide better quarterback protection. Roger had thrown several passes that should have been caught. Coach Rhode did not scold them.

He appealed to the players. The coach spoke to each player, first telling them what they had done well and encouraging them to keep up the good work. Next, he talked to them about things to which they should pay more attention. Never once did he criticize their play. The team returned to the field more than fired up, ready to make the coach proud.

Play resumed on the field with a tied score. Neither team had been able to move the ball across the finish line. The score between Martin Luther King High and North High was "0". It was nothing to nothing, a deadlocked game.

Henri began the third quarter firmly planted on the bench. He intently watched the team play as it unfolded on the field. Jackson had cautioned him that whether he was on the bench or the field, he was in the game.

He said, "Always pay attention so you are ready to contribute when you get into the game."

Henri would become the beneficiary of the older man's advice in the fourth quarter.

He was called into the game during the last minutes of the fourth quarter. He had noticed that the slot receivers were receiving immediate attention even before the ball was in the air. As a result, they either mishandled the ball or were immediately tackled. Adding to this ineffectiveness was the pattern of Roger's passes. Roger had mentally decided that Jeff Parker was his most effective receiver. He could be counted on to seek Jeff out as his choice even when it was obvious that Jeff was being well-guarded.

A Star is Born

Roger missed the opportunity to throw the ball to Henri for his first ten passes after he entered the game. In what was to be the final huddle of the match, Henri whispered to Roger, "I can outrun the defense, and I can catch the ball."

The opposing team had no intention of allowing Roger to get a pass off to anyone. Jeff Parker was blanketed with defensive players. Roger Thomas was scrambling and seemingly in mortal danger of his very life.

In the last seconds before the swarm of defenders converged on their quarry, Roger, in the last gasp of energy and desperation, heaved the football nearly the length of the football field. After which, he disappeared beneath the determined avalanche of defenders.

It was hard to tell if the intent was to throw the ball away to be spared the embarrassment of a sack or if it was an honest attempt to throw a pass.

'The quarterback's job is to throw the ball. Your job is to catch it. It doesn't matter how well he does his job; to be an outstanding wide receiver, you must excel in doing yours.'

In Henri's mind, the quarterback had thrown a pass, but it certainly was not a good one. As the pass began its descent toward the ground, it was obvious that its descent would carry it out of bounds. Only one hand could be used to reach it and still stay within bounds. Henri timed his leap to the last possible minute.

Stretching to the full length of his body and extending his left arm and hand, together with a 26-inch leap into the air, the left hand secured the wayward ball. Without breaking stride, Henri ushered the ball into the zone. The score was now "6" to "0" in favor of Martin Luther King High School.

The game ended abruptly as the time ran out at the same moment Henri crossed the opposing goal line. Following Coach Rhode's instructions, Roger took a knee instead of kicking the extra point. By then, the bleachers had come alive with some idea of what had just happened. North High, who were pushing for overtime in which they would go away victorious, was stunned into silence. Martin Luther King fans were still unsure if they should believe they had won. But they yelled anyway and, at the same time, tried to get verification from each other of their victory.

No one could have been happier for her son's success on the football field than Sara Harris. At the same time, she was apprehensive at the unseen but very real avalanche of evils that could try to tempt him. Coach Rhode had warned the team that success would draw the attention of those best avoided.

Unbeknownst to their families, Henri and Donna had passed the sexual temptation test with flying colors. But Jackson Brown counseled the evils of the promise of big-time money. His advice was firsthand, passionate, and extensive. Henri considered his advice given as surrogates of Henry Senior's advice that could and must be heeded with the same logic and will he and Donna had experienced.

Humility

Coach Rhode had been running down the sideline and arrived at the end zone shortly after Henri. Aware of the great strain that Henri had just exerted on his body, the coach feared injury. "Are you hurt? Boy, are you hurt?" he inquired as he neared the end zone. Being assured that no damage had taken place, he directed the other coaches, who by now had caught up with him, to see if some fast-thinking fan had snapped a picture.

This marked the second time he had witnessed Henri make a one-handed catch. But this was the first time he had witnessed anyone make a catch as Henri had just made.

Violating his own rule about player contact, Coach Rhode genuinely embraced Henri. Not only because they had won the game against North but because of the great effort it had taken on Henri's part. In Coach Rhode's mind, such ability deserved special rules.

Jackson Brown had said to give credit from your heart. Start at the highest and go to the lowest. But never give credit to yourself. For Henri, that meant praising God, glory to Coach Rhode without forgetting the other coaching staff members, distinction to teammates, and recognition to his family, including his mother and father.

This was the same logic he and Donna used when confronting the demons of temptation and lust in the park. The credit for their success then belonged to the character of Donna and his parents.

Henry Sr. was always there in Henri's mind. His memory was present in all his decision-making. Henri vowed to credit his mom and give his dad flesh and blood credit whenever he could.

The eight games that made up the football season were soon played, and the season ended. For Henri, the last seven games were carbon copies of the first. Roger had learned to always look down the field when he could not find a receiver. Henri always tried to be there. He had followed Jackson's advice: always make yourself available to catch the ball.

Following that advice, he often showed up in places the opposing team no doubt thought he shouldn't be. It had been a great season, and as Coach Rhode had predicted, he had become famous, at least at Martin Luther King High School.

Prom Night

Prom night filled Henri's heart with dread. He had voiced the thought that he would not go at all. The answer came back with his mother's calm assurance that everything would work out. The problem wasn't that he could not get a date. The problem was that he did not want a date.

Who knew how the line of communication was wired across the country to other high schools? To Donna's high school?!

After all, he had received her congratulations for receiving the Honor Society Award. She had sent little notes of congratulations on his football successes. All this without his having written one word about the goings on at Martin Luther King Jr. High. He did not want any bad publicity. He mused no news travels as fast as bad news, and public school news was among the fastest.

He and Donna had never declared themselves to be "going steady." Apart from the awakening in the park, there had never been a formal declaration of engagement. Their formal declaration of love for one another was deep and sincere. Both had felt within themselves that it was everlasting. Henri remembered the words that he had spoken: We must wait. The phrase indicated that what had transpired in the park was not final. A conclusion was yet to be played out in their lives. More than that, Henri mused. The phrase indicated that their relationship was continuous, forever.

He thought the best way to avoid bad publicity was not to give it a place to take root. He would go to the prom alone. He did not need to be embarrassed about not having a date. He was not being egotistical by thinking there were many girls that would be glad to be asked to the prom by him. The football season had been kind to him, and he was well-known and applauded.

It was the first time that Henri had attended a prom. The usual school garb of the young men was transformed into two-piece suits and ties. Some, apparently driven by higher aspirations, wore tuxedos with top hats. It was truly the high point of the public school experience for the graduating seniors. Henry was genuinely glad that Sara Harris had reminded him that there might be awards for honor students and athletics for the excellent year in sports that the school had experienced. It would be disappointing to the organizers if those who helped contribute to the school's success were absent.

Henri was unsurprised that the prom program attested to his mother's cautions. He was asked to stand with the Honor Society members. Standing before the assembly, they asked that the students they were recommending to the Honor Society come forward. It was a proud and gratifying moment for Henri. His recommendation was Jackson Brown's daughter, Christine. Jackson Brown had enlisted the services of his oldest son, Robert, to escort his sister to receive her award.

Coach Rhode hosted the recognition from the Athletics Department. The coach looked distinguished and was as well-dressed as the students. He was an example for every young man to strive to emulate. And a model for every young lady to look for in a mate. He gave genuine appreciation for the contributions of each department. They were naming several students by name and handing out intermediate awards designated by their coaches.

Coach Rhode held the football team until the end. He was the head of the Football Department and, therefore, could speak personally about it. He was careful not to let his recognition of one individual overshadow the contribution of another. At the same time, he was able to let his deep-felt gratitude be expressed.

The final honor he was to bestow elicited a gasp from the audience. He announced an award not made lightly at the high school level—the retirement of football jerseys. Jersey numbers 10 and 23 belonging to the quarterback, Roger Thomas, and the wide receiver, Henri Harris, are to be retired.

The jerseys would always be displayed in the school gymnasium. Each of the young men was asked to stand, which they did and waved at the audience, and sat back down. The coach, ever aware and empathic to the feelings of others, accepted this jester as appropriate and enough and let them off the hook.

Graduation

Graduation day arrived with all the pomp and circumstance you would expect after twelve years of public school. Add to that the two or three years of preparatory schooling. Henri calls those the getting-me-ready years. They depended on how brilliant your parents thought you to be or wanted you to become. Henri, the only child in the Harris household, was swept along with the tide of tasks that graduation demands. The robe and cape had to be returned because they were for a five-foot-four inch instead of a six-foot-four graduate. Pictures of graduates had to be taken, and tickets for parents and friends to attend the graduation ceremony had to be purchased.

This was an especially important day for Sara Harris. She had followed the model left by Henry Sr. By all appearances, the graduation would signal that her job was complete. Henry had grown up in what the world called a single-parent home. But Henri and Sara knew Henry Sr. was very much alive in the Harris home. Yet Sara knew that finding traction on the slippery slopes of adult life required a helping hand. Her job would not be complete until she had accomplished that last major task for Henri.

Because of his membership in the National Honor Society, Henri was one of three members of the Honor Society asked to present words of encouragement to graduating students. When presented with this honor, Henri did not allow his natural inclination to refuse such tasks to stand in his way. This would be an excellent opportunity for him to give credit to the many mothers present, especially his mother, who were daily assaulted instead of assisted in raising their children. It would also be a platform to credit his deceased father as a model and motivator for Henri to succeed.

83

Henri would be well supported by personal friends and friends of the Harris family. It became more apparent how important Henri's success was to the Harris community. It became even clearer when Jackson Brown shared with Henry that he and Martin Luther King High School's mothers used him as a model. Jackson's children reported to their father that the phrase " Be like Henri Harris" was heard so much that the words were ended by the offender, "Like Henri Harris."

Henri didn't need to secure tickets for the graduation ceremony for his school friends, as all enrolled seniors would be automatically issued tickets. His list included Jackson Brown and his wife Brenda, a ticket each for Robert, Mark, and Christine Brown. In addition, Jackson Brown had asked for several additional tickets for his former Cleveland Brown Football teammates. At his mother's request, Henri also secured tickets for Judith Waverly, Reverend Bernard P. Wise, Pastor of the Enoch Baptist Church, and several of Reverend Wise's parishioners. Henri felt pleased with what he called a respectable number of supporters, both in number and quality.

At last, the big day arrived, graduation day. Sara Harris was dressed in a new suit. She was probably the prettiest mother present, according to Henri's calculations. Henri and his fellow graduates were all dressed in their best attire. Some young men are fumbling in new suits and wearing ties for the first time. Young girls in high heels didn't seem to allow their ankles to support them uprightly. The most amusing thing about the predicament of dealing with the unfamiliar was the common graduation dress - The graduation robes. They covered all the finery, pomp, and circumstance of the students' foreign fashion.

The graduation service started with the usual introduction of officials. The introduction of dignitaries began according to etiquette and proceeded with whoever was deemed socially appropriate. From there to the graduates, the process seemed like forever. Finally, all the dignitaries and those deserving of recognition were introduced. It was time for presentations.

Henri was a close observer of events and actions in which he would be called upon to participate. He was extremely pleased that when Miss Barnett announced the speakers for encouragement, he was the last to speak. Those who spoke first and second set the example. Henri felt that he had ample leeway to express himself fully.

After having covered the usual obligations of a public speaker and giving credit to the two speakers that preceded him, Henri began:

"A few weeks following my fourth year of age, I became an orphan, my father having died in an automobile accident. As a male, I can attest to the life-altering consequences it brings to a boy's life. Although I can only speak for the male side of this equation, I am sure this trauma is similar for girls.

I employ the less commonly used word orphan to describe the loss of one parent. In my case, a father, to emphasize that I still have a mother who had been married to my father.

The question of my pedigree has been questioned throughout my public school life by both teachers and students. My purpose this evening is to bring relief to the population of orphans in our public schools, whether orphaned by death, sickness, separation, abandonment, or any other circumstance that separates them from a parent.

My mother's every waking hour has been to raise me to be every bit the man my father was. Through the years, my father has been the model and my mother the caretaker of it. I thank God my father married a woman who is better than an excellent mother.

My advice to graduating ladies of Martin Luther King Jr High School is to marry a man that will be an excellent father to their children, whether they be present or absent from home." With that, Henri thanked the audience and his fellow students and took his seat. The applause was deafening, and many fellow students stood and called his name as if calling for an encore.

At Jackson Brown's insistence, Henri's entire entourage met at French Cafe for dinner as guests of him and his family. Reverend Bernard Wise blessed the table and gave expressions and insight that only a skilled man of God could provide. To Henry, Reverend Wise seemed to know how each person present had contributed to bringing this event, meaning Henri's twelve years of school, to a successful and joyful conclusion. Reverend Wise's remarks included Jackson Brown's out-of-town guest, who he exposed as scouts for well-known NFL football teams.

Sara Harris did not have to verbalize her joy. Henri had never seen his mother so outgoing and relaxed. The worried creases that always lurked at the corner of her eyes were gone. In their place was the face of a completely simple woman. One who had finished her course, completed her task, or nearly finished it. No one would contest the conclusion that she had raised a young man. Whatever his future, Henri was equipped to handle the collision of the attributes that had sustained him with the broader society.

The Years of Grace

At his mother's insistence, Henri had taken up residence in what had passed for his father's office. With the hustle and bustle of graduation having passed, Henri's mind had turned to the questions at hand. Miss Barnett's caution concerning academic scholarships came true. The bottom line was that he might be more successful later this year or next. The prospect of such delays, six months or a year, was totally unacceptable to Henri. He needed to get started right now or seek immediate employment.

"Your Daddy had life insurance," his mother had explained years ago. This was why she had to work only a part-time job. The small home belonged to her now, and the old Honda still tried to make its forecast longevity of forever come true. The woman harbored no concerns except for the future of her son. For this particular issue, she had no capacity for other thoughts. Girls, cars, money, clothes, sports, and college; she did her best to guide her son through life's maze, no-father-be-darned.

Forty-five days were all it took for Henri to realize that college was unaffordable for him. At the last minute, the promised football scholarship had gone to a blue California chipper. That meant that his mother would have to work full-time if he was to attend. His mother, working full-time, told him that his father had not adequately provided for his family. The latter was profoundly unacceptable to a son clinging to an image of a man he knew only from photographs and his mother's recollections of his success on his first midterm.

Despite his success on his first mid-term, Henri withdrew the day after he learned his mother had applied at the factory. It would have been law, courtroom law, not the kind at which those skilled in pushing paper excel. The type of law where the winner and loser are fully identified. Fighting without fists. Legal wrestling over common issues in a high and honored venue. That was the field the boy had selected, and circumstances had forced him to abandon.

"Time plays no part in the outcome—except to force a conclusion."

☐ Henry Harris Sr.

Henry Senior had displayed these words over the wall of his small den (original author unknown), but he would be dead before his son could understand them. According to his mother, it was a quote, yet to no one was it ever attributed. Henri felt these simple words were key to his father's way of thinking. Since nowhere else could he find evidence of anything not first filtered through his mother, he reasoned that she didn't understand what his father was trying to say.

Henri mused that his grandmother could have helped to unlock the meaning of the words in his father's den. He remembered meeting his grandmother at his sixth birthday celebration.

She had been a caring and insightful person. She seemed to know just what a six-year-old wanted to know about his father. She had volunteered all that a boy his age could fathom. If only the stroke that took her consciousness had been delayed a few years. Now, this once elegant woman lay in a nursing home, unaware of her visitors as well as her memories.

Henri had never known his grandfather, though his grandmother had provided a linkage between his father and grandfather. The love and caring that his father and grandfather had in common for each other and people in general. She had said they both loved people and their children. Henry realized years later that his grandmother had planted what he called 'seeds for remembering' during that one too-brief meeting.

She was truly a gifted and loving woman. Aside from his grandmother sharing and the unsubstantiated stories of his mother, there was nothing to give life to the countless photos kept randomly in the unused closet.

Job Hunting

Opening the door had always been tricky when one needed to be silent. Henry, a large young man of 24 years, turned the old knob with the same unsuccessful deception he had attempted throughout the past two decades.

"Henry, did you get the job, boy?"

The voice was more broken than in the past, yet his reply would not be as unique.

"No, Mama, I didn't get it. I don't need that job; no way."

"Well, that's all right. There'll be more jobs in the paper tomorrow."

The baseless optimism of the woman had once been refreshing when the man was clearly a boy. Now, her words seemed shallow mocking her son like a harassing fly.

One more summer night would be consumed with his efforts to convince himself of his manhood. One more morning was doomed to greet the ill-spirited child of a desperately calm mother. Was it her fault that he had no father? Was the argument that had caused his father to storm out of the house and into a fatal car accident the responsibility of this woman, or was he—the boy—to blame? His mother never disclosed the nature of the argument, which did nothing to settle the issue.

Finding comfort in the room's darkness, Henri rehearsed his genealogy as he had done a million times before when assaulted by the demons of doubt. "I once had a father," it started. "My father is dead from a standard and acceptable means. I am not the product of some MacDaddy, spreading sperm around the neighborhood without regard. My father was Henry C. Harris Sr. of Cleveland— my mother's husband." Henri had repeated these words a hundred times during impending failure or smoldering anger.

As advertised, the morning was no friend. Retracing the motions of a thousand previous days, Henri removed himself from the bed far beyond his mother's preferred hour. It was always the sound of the shower that signaled that her child-only child was active. If she didn't hear this sound by 8 AM, she was sure to announce her concern from outside her son's bedroom door. Today, she knew Henri needed time to regroup before taking another stab at the job market, so she resisted.

The warm water saturated his brown skin. His bathroom had no shower—a luxury he preferred—therefore, he was forced to triple his time under the nozzle to get a similar effect.

It was always an understanding spray, water that seemed to know that he was better than his circumstances, water that needed no excuses because his reasoning was as clear to it as it was to him. It flowed over his hardened body as if it had cut the groves that defined his powerful physique—softening his skin to wrinkles, linking him to more pleasant days past.

The repressively small confines of the shower were the same as when the young man was a boy. They were no different today than when he might hear his mother call to him from the breakfast table. His father had called him down in much the same manner—so claimed his mother. She recalled past happenings to the extent that memories began to inculcate in the unsure mind of her son. Unless he was talking at age three, there was more than a little doubt about the authenticity of her claim. Despite Henri having reached his full maturity, the shower remained the refuge it had been when imagined night terrors motivated him into hiding within it.

In the wake of immediate failure, the young man allowed his mind to slide back through time in search of a place he knew better as a boy, and the distinction once more became clouded in his mind. In its investigation, his mind remembered how a simple accident of birth had made an unknown newcomer instantly welcome.

His arrival at Martin Luther King Jr. public school from a rocky exit from North High School was such a time. A reality that was as clear as the second day of gym class. He was big, blessed; his mother described—uncommon was the doctor's term. Whatever adjective you chose, it had made him an instant celebrity at the time.

"My big ass doesn't need this," he thought while applying soap to his body. "That chump ain't ever walked behind nothing like this. And he interviewed me?"

"Too bad they don't ask about that at the interview," he said to himself. "They sure don't."

But they never seem to get around to the one question that might distinguish the young man within the job pool, leaving his mother as the only gainfully employed member of the Harris family.

It was while contemplating absent memories from his father's chair that Henri heard the call. He had mail, which was neither common nor unusual. Nevertheless, this summons was such that he sensed an urgency in his mother's voice.

"Look," she said, a multitude of information pouring from her single syllable.

The large envelope was addressed to Hank Harris Jr., with a return address of the Littlefield Indemnity Company of Philadelphia. Reading the words for a second time, Henri could not detect his mother's cause for near hysteria. Still, she stood beside him with hands covering her mouth, transmitting the vibes of a woman in extreme anxiety.

"That's your Daddy's writing! Jesus, Lord; God, that's Hanky!"

The hysteria was lost to Henri until he read the first of what would be thousands of words.

"Son."

The word was the one he had hoped to hear all of his life. Not from his mother, but in the low-pitched resonance of the voice he now fully pictured in his mind, "Son." With a tinge of southern cotton, the words danced in his ears until there was room for the next.

"I'm writing this letter because my dad died a long time before you were born. All of my life, I wondered about him until it seemed I couldn't stand it no more. The fever that took him he got in a Montgomery factory. That's probably why I moved to Kansas. They wouldn't let me see him until it was certain he was dying. He never woke up. I swore I would never do that to a son—die on him—but sometimes things happen without cause. My father killed three men in a fair fight, except for the fact that there were three of them. I know he fought that fever even harder not to leave me.

It's obvious to me that you're special. Not for any reason in particular, but you are. I knew it clearly from the start. In your eyes, I see a sense of things I don't see anywhere else. But you're just a pup. I can't wait to see those eyes later on "

As fragmented as a pile of newspaper clippings, the page's only display of order came in their adherence to chronology. Even if scratched on a napkin, the entry was properly dated and sequenced within the stack.

"I have to go," Henri announced to his still-speechless mother. "I have to go."

Without thought of symbolism, the man guided himself to the reconditioned closet that had once served as his father's den. This time, it was not to be close to the belongings of a man he could not remember. This time, it was not to sit in the simple leather chair. But following the few words on the first page, the world contained no other place in which he could exist.

The few words written so long ago may well have been recorded at the desk where Henri sat. They were most likely penned from one of the old pens that had long since run dry. As he read into the night, each new page became its own reason not to stop. Hundreds of handwritten pages contained a story, or stories, not at all connected to the other pages. But the boy could not stop reading.

"Happy birthday, son. There is a big deal. I made a raise at the garage, so Christmas looks good this year. Raises don't really matter, though. If you're working for somebody else—you got a problem. By the time you start remembering, we'll be independent—at my own place over in Braxton.

I know I ain't got to say this, but these words ain't for your mother. If I wanted her to read them, I'd give them to her. She's a good woman, but she's still a woman. All a woman can be is just that. To ask more is to try to change nature. She doesn't work because she looks after you. Once we're in Braxton, we'll have a few more, and she won't be working either. Without your mother, I would not be where I have been, where I am and will be."

With only the occasional interruption for sandwiches and the brief trips to the restroom, Henri was diligent in reading each word of each page. The content of the comments was of such magnitude that the boy could not read and digest the information collected before him. Insights into all things were present. Never fully harboring the thought that the words would ever be used for the purpose for which they were written. Henry Sr. had afforded himself indiscriminate honesty.

Most preachers are punks. Any man telling you how powerful God is should be out using that power. If that ain't the case, a punk.

In two days, each page had been read twice. Henry emerged from the small room, still in shock. Finding nothing after the last page, all Henri could do was start over again. There was no conclusion. The pages simply truncated, ended, and ceased to continue. About a week before the accident, there were words on the power of prayer, then there was nothing except a note from the insurance company.

The insurance document was standard fare except for a short, handwritten sentence apologizing for their tardiness. It stated only that they were carrying out the last wishes of their client, Henry C. Harris Sr. From the short letter, it was clear that Mr. Harris had intended for the packet to be delivered to his son in conjunction with his eighteenth birthday. But with no explanation, this scenario was nearly 15 years behind schedule.

"You gonna let me see that letter, aren't you?" Henri's mother asked cautiously.

"I don't think so, Mom. Maybe," he said, reaching for a jacket.

"What are you getting ready to do now?"

"I've got an interview for that legal clerkship downtown."

"I didn't know you had an interview with them?"

"Neither do they, Mom. Neither do they."

The world would be no more kind, success no more assured, and pain no less severe. Some of what might happen would happen. But unlike the past 25 years, it will happen to the son of Henry C. Harris Sr. no longer one apparition sired by another.

Sara Harris knew what she had struggled to do for the past two decades as the curator of her husband, and her common dreams had come true. Henri worked with the culture he had developed through the years to survive in a cruel society pitted against entry-level gatekeepers of an established industrial society.

A community of intolerance and ignorance that demanded complete compliance insured by turf protectors more interested in self-preservation than corporate betterment. Henry Sr. had provided the last stroke needed to allow Henri Jr. to escape the slippery bounds of boyhood and sour into the heavenliness of manhood. Sara, permitting herself a bit of a sorted expression, mused that she and Henry Sr. had done a damn good job.

Returning home from a long day of job interviews, Henri fairly yanked the tattletale doorknob that had terrorized the boy through the years. Henri did not wait for his mother's customary impatience to know the results of his day's search. Instead, in a loud and joyful voice, he shouted:

"I got the job; I am the new Legal Clerk for Jackson-Johnson and Wise!"

The voice of his mother was as calm and accepting as ever: "I knew the Lord had something for you!"

Henri settled down at his father's desk with the recent events and began to think of it as his desk. Henri's mind drifted back through the years. He was only 25, looking at 26, but it seemed he had traveled a million miles. Much had transpired in those miles. Things that could have meant that he had given up and taken the easy way. His dad's notes had said, "I would not be where I have been or where I am and will be."

'I am sure glad that Henry Sr. married my mom,' Henri thought, 'a good strong Christian woman.'

With the major things of life seemingly put to rest, Henri began to think about Henri Harris, the man. With that, Donna instantly came to mind. He had not heard from her in over a year. Donna's neighborhood mole had surely told her about the prom, how he had come unescorted and had received awards. She would know about his football stardom and his presentation at graduation. Maybe the mole had moved away. Still, Donna would know other friends who would serve as a school conduit and his activities. Girls like to gossip.

Regardless of why he hadn't heard from Donna, Henri would wait for her. She had said she loved Henri, and he believed her.

Whatever had happened to her, it would take more than a phone call or a piece of paper to change that. Donna would have to tell him to his face before he would believe it. Amid his resolve, he heard the call to get to the door.

The interruption was more than a little disturbing. Reluctantly, he went to the door, and the door flew open with a yank that threatened to remove it from its hinges.

And there she was!

And then she was in his arms, kissing him, and he kissing her back without a word being spoken.

"Who is it? Henri?" Henri's mother asked.

Henri replied over his shoulder without either of them relinquishing their grip on the other. They were still standing in the open doorway; not a word had been spoken. Finally, as he loosened his grip to guide her to his father's den, she whispered,

"I waited."

And he replied,

"So did I."

THE END

Made in the USA
Middletown, DE
04 April 2024

52581441R00056